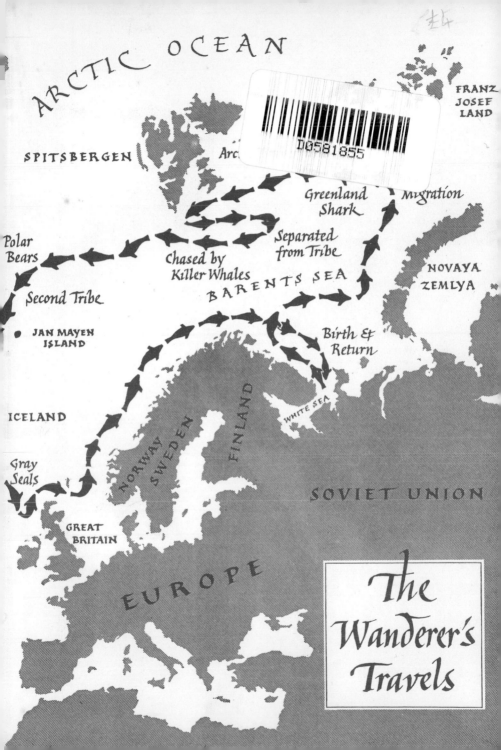

A Seal's World

FRANK STUART

A Seal's World

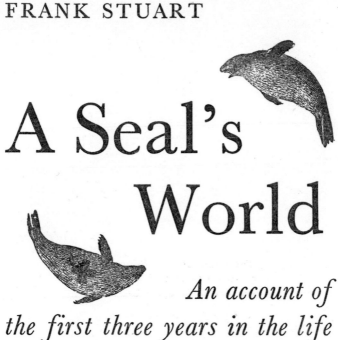

*An account of
the first three years in the life
of a harp seal   - -   illustrated by
Walter Ferguson*

GEORGE G. HARRAP & CO. LTD
LONDON TORONTO WELLINGTON SYDNEY

First published in Great Britain 1954
by GEORGE G. HARRAP & CO. LTD
182 High Holborn, London, W.C.1

*Composed in Baskerville type and printed by
Western Printing Services Ltd, Bristol
Made in Great Britain*

To
Bernhard and Ruth von Limburger

who said, one summer's day at Reutti,

" The next one must be about a seal!"

Here it is—with my love

Acknowledgments

THIS book is an adventure story. It never pretends to be a work of zoology. None the less, through observation and through the co-operation of many experts, care has been taken to give a true picture of a harp-seal's life. Invaluable assistance and advice have been generously given by many naturalist friends and also by:

The American Museum of Natural History, New York;
The British Fur Trade Alliance (Mr P. Parratt), London;
The British Museum (Natural History), especially the Staff of the Zoological Library;
The Fouke Fur Company, St Louis;
The Hudson's Bay Company, London;
Dr H. R. Lillie, Broughty Ferry, Dundee;
The Ministry of Agriculture and Fisheries, London;
The G. C. Rieber Company, Bergen, and Mr Birger Rasmussen;
The Society for Cultural Relations with the U.S.S.R.;
The United States Department of the Interior, Fish and Wild Life Service (Dr Victor B. Scheffer);
The Zoological Society, London;

and especially by Dr Erling Sivertsen, Director of Det Kgl. Norske Videnskabers Selskab Museet, Trondheim, the world's principal authority on the biology of the harp seal, who with such spontaneous kindness put at my disposal the results of his twelve years' investigations in the White Sea area, and has loaned photographs which will illustrate this book in many countries of the world.

F. S.

Contents

Illustrations

1. Ice Orphan

THE Frost King's world glittered in the moonlight. Snow-covered ice-floes, winking as if heaped with jewels, moved through black water while the north wind piped and boomed.

Some of the ice-hills were chiselled into fantastic shapes. Hummocks, with one side silver and the other shadowy black, contained ultramarine caves with pillars of pure crystal. In some of these caves frozen stalactites hung from the roofs, and mushrooms of ice with slender, pearly stalks grew from the floor. Things were moving, swaying, swinging, so that moony lights flashed and went out, and sudden seas of silver came, vanished, and shone again.

As though it could smell alarm in the rising storm, the harp-seal cub screamed with a nervous shrilling note. This was repeated by others until the March night seemed filled with orchestrations of furious wind, treble cries, the crash and crack of ice, and the plash of waves.

The whole north-west sky was tinged with a reddish-purple colour, which glowed and paled and glowed again, like the forge of Polar gods. Elsewhere the horizon was yellow-white, where the moonlight beat back from pack-ice on to continents of cloud. Light shone steadily from the moon, reflecting back from the ice-fields, and back again from the moving skyscapes.

A cloud put out the moon, and in that sudden darkness white crests of great seas rose and burst with a roar into phosphorescent spray. The ice-floes, glimmering ghostly white, slid past each other with lapping, grinding noises, and the seals' chorus of screams and cries suddenly increased as the white or grey-white cubs crept to and fro in terror, seeking a furry flank under which to hide from what was coming.

The harp-seal cub, who will be called the Wanderer, because in the three years of her adventures in this book she travelled more than ten thousand miles, was less than two weeks old on this night of Arctic tempest. About three feet long, she was coated in two-layer fur, whose outer part was just beginning to moult away around her head and flippers. This outer coat, two inches long, was pure white and soft, while the inner layer of pale grey, almost an inch long, intensely thick, and at this stage very curly, was just beginning to come into view.

The cub was almost as round as a ball. Under that double fur coat was a thick layer of blubber she had put on by digesting seal-milk containing more than twelve times as much fat and four times as much protein as cow's milk—a baby-food looking like thick cream. Lying still for a moment, staring over the edge of a hole in the ice-floe, she herself looked like a blown drift of snow, except for her jet-black muzzle and dark eyes peering anxiously down. Again, suddenly alarmed by the howling wind and the sharper movements of the swimming ice under her, she uttered a piercing cry, between the call of a cat, a dog, and a lamb—
Ma–a–a–a–a!

Abruptly a female seal's head popped out of the hole, glancing round for danger with the swift competence evolved when a mistake means death. It looked each way round the pup's body before its liquid eyes rested briefly on that obstacle. Then, without malice or sentimentality, it knocked the youngster over, hurled itself from the hole like a dark torpedo, and thrust across the ice to its own cub.

Before the Wanderer could scramble, whimpering, up-right two more mother seals had shot out of the hole, which was barely wide enough to let their bodies pass, and had a rounded rim of ice at the top formed from the thin ice that they dragged up on their bodies from the layer that had congealed on the water in the hole.

The next newcomer was the Wanderer's mother, and the white pup flung herself against the saddle-shaped mark that showed faintly on the grey fur. All she got for her babyish eagerness was a sharp shove from her mother's head. The mother seals were ill-tempered after ten or twelve days' suckling while they had themselves gone almost without food. Now the shouting wind and the strange tremors of the ice-floe were breeding panic. An instinct in every nerve warned them to get away from the grinding ice into safe, deep water. But another more powerful impulse forced them to answer the screams of the frightened cubs.

The Wanderer's mother repeated the blow unmeaningly. Then she struck again, this time with purpose, half butting and half driving the cub towards the edge of the floe. The distance was only a few yards. The place was marked by a line of deeper black from which the sea climbed and spun in the darkness. But the movement to escape was too late. With a thunderous crash the long ship of ice grounded, just where the currents were strongest on an undersea shoal.

The force of the impact was terrific, splitting the floe in several directions like a pane of glass. Seals went slithering along the surface, the young ones bawling, the mothers grimly silent, trying to cling with powerful nails while their solid world broke under them. Far down into the water the middle of the ice-floe stretched its nightmare shape; on the surface, hummocks rose to thirty feet like castle-turrets. But now the whole mass was collapsing from the stupendous undersea concussions.

The northern gale was shoving one way; with irresistible pressure the current was running the other way. Not only this floe but hundreds of others along the edge of the ice-pack commenced a slow and monstrous motion, screwing, piling, rafting, and sliding up on edge.

Most of the baby seals were too young to trust themselves to the furious sea at the edges of the floes, where smashed ice churned and leapt. Their mothers savagely tried to bunt them into the water, while the terrified youngsters attempted to claw a way towards the middle of the floe. First here, then there, a seal-mother would turn away, overwhelmed by fear, leave her baby to fend for itself, and hurtle as fast as a running man towards the leaping sea. A plunge and they were gone, the clumsy, dragging thing of a moment ago changed into a supple shadow in the depths of the sea, faster than a fish, to dodge the gap-toothed rushes of the plunging ice.

The Wanderer's mother, opposed with obstinate cunning, tried to seize the cub in her jaws and drag her. But on the breaking ice the mother could not do what would have been easy in the sea. With a roaring noise another ice-island struck the floe, and from it came a new appalling outcry of helpless young seals. At that the Wanderer's mother turned like a flash to dive down the hole in the ice up which she had come.

It was no longer there. Squeezed by thousands of tons' pressure from the new floe, the hole had closed along a fissure-edge which was beginning to rise ominously through the darkness. With a sound that was half a grunt and half a sob, the seal mother turned and slithered away in the dark.

Alarmed at her mother's disappearance, the white cub turned to shove herself the way the other had gone. But the ice twisted bodily under her, and a new white wall suddenly rose in her path like a striking monster. With a scream the cub turned this way and that, panic clouding all instinctive movements of escape. First here, then there in the darkness, the ice-hammers rose over the floundering little body.

The cub shoved herself about like a dog with broken fore-legs. As she went she screamed for the comforting and furry maternal side. Minutes passed and lengthened to hours, and the hours dragged out towards an Arctic dawn. No mother came. Finally the pup's terror at the splitting and smashing and the battering-ram thuds and shudders faded slowly into weariness and a sort of stunned acceptance of the new conditions of her fortnight-old life.

She lay still at last, too exhausted to move, in the shadow of a twenty-foot hummock on a thick central part of the floe which still resisted the screwing and grinding of the ice about it. This hummock had been formed in some previous winter by just such a storm as this one, when ice, rafting up on end on top of other ice, had frozen solidly into place.

When the dawn came faintly across the white world that was still leaping fantastically, the baby seal saw another whitecoat, pressed flat under a sliding tongue of ice, frozen in its glazed coffin. Another cub lay on its side with its head crushed by a block that had cracked off the summit of the hummock and struck it before bounding away. There were dead whitecoats everywhere, mostly small ones less than a week old who had no understanding of danger. Other motherless cubs were dismally shrieking. But they were left unattended. No mother seals would come until the turbu-lence of the slush-ice had subsided.

The Wanderer cried out as vehemently as any. She was a strong cub, born of big and healthy parents, well nourished, and she had already tried in a puppyish way to swim. But neither to her nor to any others on the remnant of the ice-island did the mother seals make their way back that morning.

The wind was still rising. A watery Arctic sun glittered blindingly on the dance of the ice-floes. By daylight it was obvious that great numbers of cubs had been killed. More were slaughtered every hour as they tried feebly to creep this way or that. Ice reared over them, or cracks opened under their bodies and then clashed together on them. The shattering impacts of new floes skidded them into the sea, to drown if they had not learned to swim, or to crush them between moving blocks.

Soon after daylight a flock of big white birds came, ivory gulls, sailing and gliding between the floes, balancing themselves in beauty on the wind against the pale, blue-patched, cloud-streaming sky. Down flew the birds, spotless save for dark beaks and feet and black carmine-ringed eyes. Harshly screaming, they settled on the mangled bodies of the baby seals, dipped rapaciously, then lifted scarlet beaks.

The seal-pups left alive took no notice of the birds, or of their own dead companions. They cried out unceasingly against the uproar of the wind and the crash and grind of the screwing ice, instinctively uttering those calls which had always hitherto brought them warmth, food, and security.

Towards midday the wind began to subside, and the first seal-mother came swimming out to the island, twisting past the smashing ice. She put her head up swiftly to look for a place to draw herself on to the remnant of the floe, dived when half an acre of ice tumbled at her, emerged again after five minutes in quite a different place, dived, then reappeared suddenly, clawing herself up on to the broken island. She shoved herself along with her hind-flippers, accidentally scattering the birds from their bloody feast, and went past the Wanderer to another cub, whose cries were instantly stilled. Five minutes later a second seal clambered on to the ice. Then another, and then more.

To each one the Wanderer lifted her head, and towards one or two she began uncertainly to shove herself with that strange action that arouses in men's minds the idea of a mermaid, crippled ashore, but perfect when turning in the water. The seal-mothers ignored this questing pup, shoving past her as if she was not there, knocking her out of the way if she happened to obstruct them, indifferent to her bawling, which was at first querulous, then plaintive, and finally urgent and pitiful.

All that day, frantic for the warm comfort of her accustomed milk, the cub crawled slowly about the ice-mass. She was bewildered by its new shape, finding sea-edges where yesterday had been seemingly limitless stretches of surface, or new hummocks where there had been smooth glissades. For some time she searched for the hole in the ice up which her mother used to climb from the sea. But it was gone. Towards the end of that day she tried to press herself for warmth against other cubs. But the little whitecoats crawled fretfully away, or tried half-playfully to mouth her.

As darkness fell again the wind dropped to a breeze, and the screwing of the ice-floes ceased. But that did not help the mother of the Wanderer, who lay crushed out of shape on the sea-bottom below the under surface of the ice.

She had delayed her rush to escape just a shade too late. For such errors of judgment indifferent Nature exacts a common penalty from us all.

B

2. The Painted Cub

FOR some days and nights after her mother's death the Wanderer remained on the broken remnant of the ice-floe. At first she whimpered when she saw other cubs suckling. Sometimes she tried to steal milk, only to be knocked over in the snow. Then she grew resigned to this foodless and motherless dispensation, crept about the ice, and mouthed playfully at strange cubs. She was living quite comfortably on the thick layer of blubber that baby-milk had laid on under her skin. Meanwhile she absorbed intense impressions, the sum of which became a magnetic force that always afterwards inexorably drew her towards this place at the entrance to the White Sea, no matter where else she went.

The March weather, cleared by the storm, grew dazzling. The ice-fields spread illimitably, covered with snow beneath a cloudless sky of pale blue. Along the edge of the ice-pack were promontories, bays, and leads of water. Here floes slowly drifted, bearing countless seals, so that often they seemed like solid masses of darker colour stretching as far as the eye could see. The floes floated quietly north with the wind and the current an average of several miles a day, some going two hundred miles during the brief whelping season. They travelled fast or slowly according to their sizes and depths.

The orphaned cub ran increasingly often to the edge of the floe and stared at the open water. It throbbed continually with thousands of seals, snorting, splashing, racing along the surface, then diving all together out of sight. Their movements were so co-ordinated that often it seemed as though they were playing some strict water-game. Then a gleaming head would appear over the edge of a floe, a seal's five-and-a-half-foot length would flounder ashore and go sinuously across the ice towards her pup, perhaps sniffing at one or two others as she passed.

Having found her baby, she would lie sleekly on her side and suckle it. Sometimes she would fall asleep. Yet every few minutes during that sleep her head would lift and she would glance around for danger. As her baby nuzzled into her she would stroke it idly with her fore-flipper, smoothing its fur.

Sometimes when the cub was very young the mother's mate would come out of the sea and lie beside her, his handsome harp-like saddle-mark showing black on his back and sides. The trio would make a pretty family group. Harp-seals are monogamous, and are affectionate towards their mates. When the cub was a little older the father would join a male party of a dozen or so, swimming or congregating on the ice to laze and sunbathe. They would scratch themselves now and then, and blink mildly seaward, careless of the constant screeching from unsatisfied pups on the nursery slopes. Whiskery expressions of satisfaction would show on their drowsy faces.

Idling time away, they would move off together, plunge heartily into the sea, and begin again the complicated diving and racing which filled so much of their days. Sometimes they would sleep in the water, keeping themselves afloat with their hind-flippers as subconsciously as breathing.

The Wanderer watched them intently. She often began a half-hearted rush at the water, copying theirs, only to stop short at the edge of the floe. She had gone swimming once with her mother, and swimming sensations came and went in her body. As she eyed the others she arched or stretched herself, imitating their movements as they flashed past below her in the sea. The excitement she felt when watching the swimming steadily increased like a pulse in the blood, growing louder and harder till it was unbearable. She lifted her face and looked out again and again over the sun-glittering ripples. She peered with a swift turn of the head as a swimming shadow fled by under the surface.

Several days earlier she had been pushed into the water by her mother. Its cold shock made her shriek and blow out and splash helplessly, her mother swimming smoothly round her. Then, the first impact of terror gone, she scuttered nervously about and instinctively made a little dive. Alarmed by the water darkening over her head, she leapt to the surface again, only to see her mother slide swiftly under her and disappear into the deep. But the Wanderer had had enough for that day, and was struggling and scrambling at the ice-edge.

She could not remember these experiences, but her limbs had not forgotten what they had learned. She looked down. There was the water below, wavering and lapping. She hitched herself forward almost over the edge, tried to draw back, slithered on the slippery ice, and fell in, making a heavy splash.

And then—delight! Instead of the clumsy dragging, a swift gliding and twisting in sinuous grace. Instead of fear in slowness, the delirium of speed. She was, in fact, swimming rather clumsily, weighted by large remnants of her woolly white outer coat. But to a creature that had been earthbound this freedom, this loss of weight, and this gain of shimmering mobility, was like a new birth. In the water she was beginning her mermaid life.

It was not only that her body seemed suddenly to be lighter than air. Her eyes, with which she saw imperfectly on land, could penetrate in the different refraction of water with telescopic clarity far into the depths. And she found these depths full of exciting objects. The tactile hairs on her nose, useless on ice, now came to life, tremoring changing messages through the sensitive nerves at their roots. They told her of the movements and temperatures of water, the nearness of floes or of other seals, the volumes of air rolling before and indicating the size and motions of an oncoming wave.

She swam hilariously away and away, abandoning the ice-floe that had been all her world. Seals of all ages, veterans of six or eight years old, half-grown greys, ragged cubs like herself, popped their heads inquiringly up beside her, rolled down the depths before her, spun over and round her in all directions, inciting her to join them in water delights. She saw one swimming nose-down and tail-up and deliciously copied it. She floundered madly, yet presently achieved that position, from which she could stare down into the dimness below. Then with a flick she leapt upright once more.

Out of the deeps swam a ragged cub of her own age. Its top wool coat had shed away from the dark head and flippers and in patches from its back. This cub floated timidly past looking anxiously at her. Curiosity rose like a flood in the Wanderer, for this seal was not like the rest. He had a brightly shining metal tab on his back between his flippers at the root of his tail, like an extra eye winking and glittering. It bore a name: ZOOL. MUSEUM, OSLO, and a number. Moreover, on the grey fur on his back, where the baby wool was moulting off, was a huge red cross. It had been painted from his neck to well down towards his tail, and right across his back down his two sides.

In all creatures, even in man, who wages his wars because of it, fear of the stranger is an instinct as deep-rooted as sex or hunger. As this little cub with the extraordinary marks swam along other seals glided away to each side, leaving a clear passage. Thus it had been ever since a party of Norwegian scientists marked him three days ago, so that sealers would not kill him, but would record his number and position whenever he was afterwards seen. It is from such records that facts for all our seal-stories are gathered.

The markings perturbed the other seals, who avoided him. Because of this the cub felt uneasy and made things worse by trying to get close to the rest.

He plunged towards the Wanderer, avid for friendliness. With the insatiable inquisitiveness which was to lead her into so many adventures, and with a gaiety which later became a marked part of her character, she snaked under the stranger's body and up behind him to look again at that extra eye. The tab winked at her, the cub flashed round to face her, and she darted after his tail to see the glitter again.

So began a game of incredibly swift glide and dive, roll and return, into a sun-splash and out of it, through a wave-top and under it, ringing a floating ice-block nose to tail in one continuous streak. Always the game was patterned by her pursuit of that bright tab in his fur, and by his attempts to twist and meet her face to face. Long after the tab was quite familiar to her, this pattern of play dominated their time together.

Suddenly the stranger dived and was gone. Unwilling to lose him, the Wanderer found herself swimming deep for the first time. Her five-toed, webbed hind-limbs, so clumsy on land, now became two magnificently powerful propellers. With a lateral swing of her body and alternate strokes of the hind-feet with the web spread, she drove smoothly down, folding the web to withdraw the foot for a new stroke. Her fore-flippers fitted against her body in a depression contrived by Nature for perfect streamlining, or moved out to correct steering and balance. She had blown most of the air out of her lungs before her head went under. As she glided deeper and deeper, her heart-beat, which at the surface was about one hundred and fifty a minute, twice the rate of a man's, slowed to ten a minute. This enormously reduced the consumption of oxygen stored in her blood. The dramatic decrease in circulation, due to the slower heart-beat, quieted the whole of the little diving seal's living processes, no matter how vigorous or powerful her underwater movements might be.

In the greeny darkness of the sea fifty feet below the surface, a new playground came to life before her. Some of the ice-floes went down underwater far below this depth, and their sides were pitted with caverns, in and out of which the two youngsters played. The shadowy forms of other seals moved with tremendous swiftness past them and were gone, those tactile nose-hairs giving a sort of radar warning when other creatures approached or any obstacle lay ahead.

Then the two cubs were racing upward again, had splashed into sunlight, and were restoring with deep breaths all their physical functions to normal surface speed and power.

It was wonderful! The Wanderer lay still, quivering in the ecstasy of living. She had tasted for the first time the enjoyment that comes from the precision in high-speed movement of the million complex parts that make a healthy body.

Ahead was an ice-floe, a strange one. Another whole new world to be explored! In a moment the two cubs were scrambling on to it, pushing importantly past screaming milk-drinkers, stretching and blinking at each other in an elderly way in the sun. The Wanderer lifted her head, and touched the strange bright tab shining on the other's back. She was not afraid of it. In life she was to be afraid of few things, only seldom knowing how closely death hedged her round.

The male cub rolled over joyfully. Animals have little memory for troubles, and already he had forgotten that he had been for days an outcast. In that moment some impression formed itself in the awareness of each of these young things, and during ensuing years there were many times when one or the other lifted a head questioningly at a gleaming ice-floe whose shape resembled this one at the entrance to the White Sea.

These two stayed together as night followed day and day shadowed and darkened into night. But each grew increasingly restless and dissatisfied. Though they did not know how to assuage it, each was becoming very hungry. The thick layer of blubber built up from ten days' swallowing of seal-cream still provided a store of food on which their bodies were steadily drawing. For two weeks, eating nothing at all, they grew thinner, more mobile, more avid. They did not know how to react, except by swimming faster and diving deeper, and sparring at each other or at floating objects that went sailing slowly by.

Though the adult seals still avoided the cub marked with the big red cross, the young adventurers in the slush-ice came to him readily when they saw the Wanderer do so. Presently a young community of about twenty, some still shedding their last baby-wool, went racing through the waves together, dived into underwater caves, or lay resting on the ice.

None of the others pursued the bright tab, but the Wanderer continually did so. As the spring sun gained power day by day the surface water grew warmer, cutting deep indentations along the sea-level of the floes. Just below the surface, the water was exhilaratingly cold. The seals played in the warm layer, which was added to constantly by snow melting in the sun and running off the ice-surfaces.

A day came of streaky, clouded skies. The sun rose brilliantly, making the Polar world blinding white, beating down with a foretaste of summer strength through a thinner, clearer air. Then clouds gathered. The young seals were excited by a warmth they had never experienced before in their lives. They responded to it with redoubled dives and races, and with gyrations round and among the slush-ice.

At the height of this wildness the Wanderer noticed that

her friend lay suddenly still in the water staring along its surface. With the instant recognition of the wild that such looks mean danger, her eyes turned the same way. There, in the sky, was a strange vision.

A steamship appeared to be sailing through the clouds. A pall of smoke drifted from its funnel, and it lifted its bow over a tableland of ice, backed off, then assaulted the ice again. The apparition was silent, and would have roused no sensation in the Wanderer, other than curiosity, but for the fear with which her companion stared. With a splash he turned over and dived.

Instantly she followed him down through the translucent and then the darkening depths. They descended deeper than ever before, and moved slowly about, staying down for a long time. Frequently she began to move upward again, looking across at him. But he stubbornly stayed, moving his body to maintain his depth, and each time she swam round and down to him again. She could not tell why he was afraid—that it was because men from a ship had caught and painted him, and sewn into his skin the metal identity-tag by which to check his migrations in future years. She was not much frightened by his fear, but she stayed in the dark water slowly swinging to and fro near his side. He looked at her constantly, apparently relieved to have her near.

Meanwhile, though the other seals took no notice of it and continued playing as cheerfully as ever at the surface, the mirage remained in the sky. In reality the sealing-ship was far away. But rapid changes in the density of the air layers above it, due to the heat and to an intruding current, had bent the light rays and produced the uncanny effect of a steamship sailing in Arctic clouds.

For a long time the two young seals moved as slowly as drowned men in the deeps between the feet of the great ice-floes. Perhaps the extra strain of the long dive made them avid. They glanced restlessly up, peered below, stared round.

Then the Wanderer saw that her companion was behaving in a strange new way. A drift of almost colourless and minute shrimps was passing, and the painted cub was awkwardly mouthing at them. The Wanderer, always curious and light-hearted enough to imitate any new game, went curving into the cloud of swimming atomies and began to snap her jaws. After more than two weeks' starvation a delicious tremor ran through her, sweet and exciting, and she forgot everything except the marvel of learning how to eat.

3. *Shadow of Death*

WHEN the two seals finally splashed to the surface the mirage had faded, and the ship no longer sailed through the sky.

The extraordinary experience of eating, too, had driven fear from both of them. They had, as yet, no ability to recognize the colour, drift, temperature, and feeling of water likely to contain the shrimp-like crustacea on which, for a time, they must live. Seals migrate to the White Sea to breed, probably because in that area at that time there is a great quantity of this food vital to cubs learning to feed themselves. The initiation of these two to food other than milk excited new sensations and reactions. They dashed through the water, snapping their jaws in surprise that no food taste resulted. They imitated the dives and turns of other seals, frantic lest these should be enjoying the sensation that they had lost. They swam close to them, or followed only inches behind a sportively gliding tail.

The Wanderer had accepted with animal resignation the weeks without food after her mother's disappearance. Now, with the pale shrimps, she had eaten of the tree of knowledge, and had become aware of the aches and angers of starvation. She stubbornly trailed a much older cub into another area of sea-food, and would have been willing, for the first time since their meeting, to shake off the painted cub. But he shimmered down beside her, and there was substance enough for all. Certain peculiarities of this water made her think of her first solid meal. Always afterwards she lifted a questing nose at the first smell of such water and began to peer and feel for satisfaction and to open her mouth. She was learning one of the first lessons about how to live.

A score of young cubs, of whom she was one, formed such a group among dozens. Each group played or rested by itself, though there was a good deal of drifting from one group to another. Most of the adult seals had swum away, first to carry out an intense food foray after weeks of virtual starvation during whelping, suckling, and the mating games that followed. In these weeks their girth had been reduced by about a foot, many of the mothers losing more than a quarter of their total weight.

Absence of the elders left the growing cubs delightfully free. Almost all the white baby-fur had moulted, and their close grey fur coats were sleek and handsome. Now they could explore all the ice-floes, even those sacred places where their fathers had congregated grunting fiercely at any youthful trespass. Days and nights became a round of play, mock-challenge, feigned escape, adventure on ice or under sea.

Each day was a little longer, a little warmer, each night shorter. Obeying the crescendo of sunshine and heat, they seemed to live more fully every day. Growing strength matched the challenge of new opportunities to dive deeper, swim faster, play more wildly. Just as in warmer lands grass grows and trees unfold their leaves, so here, among the ice, animals and birds and fishes found each day growing with them, offering more as they became big enough to take more.

On a day of shouting wind and clashing ice there came

riding by gambolling hundreds into the ice-bay a countless regiment of year-old and two-year-old grey seals, the adolescents of their race which take three or four years to mature. Hilariously surfing or sinuously gliding, this horde of young dogs of the sea came pouring past. Brown-eyed heads suddenly popped out of every wave and gracefully vanished together in a spin of foam. Then they raced under the glass-green surface like a shoal of shadowy fish.

As if in bucolic fun, they mobbed and ringed the puppy-packs around, above, below, and these who had seemed so swift and elegant now looked by comparison as clumsy as if stuffed with sawdust. Excited by this to fresh fantasies of speed and turn, the big greybacks, some already the size of adults, played pranks larger and more salty than before. They burst from the depths so that the youngsters floundered back in terror, pursued each other with colossal zest, and leapt clean out of the water like great salmon, re-entering with as much splash as possible.

For a day or two the cubs and greybacks shouldered each other on the ice and in the bays among the floes. The invading elders showed no enmity beyond an occasional mock-ferocious rush or dive. Then suddenly the northern playground of the ice-field-edge was different.

The young ones kept more tightly in their groups. As if some wordless message had run among them, they turned towards the north-west. They made several excursions, returning again, then swimming faster than before along the edge of the ice. During the night they remained restless, questing ever a little farther. Some distance out they met groups of strange cubs, not gambolling but moving steadily on and on until out of sight. Into this solemn movement they were irresistibly swept, to swim at an easy three or four miles an hour away into the north-west.

They did not know where they were going, or why. No older seals led them. Like rats following an invisible Pied Piper, they swept quietly along, instinct-guided, in companies of from half a dozen to a score, neither seeking food nor looking to right or left. They journeyed on four hundred sea-miles until they plunged into the first of the great fish shoals off Eastern Finmark.

The fish were capelin. They swerved aside in frightened clouds, though these particular groups of very young seal-cubs were not yet minded to attack them seriously. Many did dash at the capelin outliers who had not turned quickly or far enough aside. There was no real effort at capture—it was a sort of ferocious play, perhaps to learn how to match the fishes' movements before starvation was the penalty for failure.

The Wanderer, whose playful ways had been irked by the long, sober miles of the journey, welcomed the diversion. She could swim like a fish herself, and she thrilled and warmed in the mock pursuits. Did the fish dive, she went down after them, the pupils of her eyes expanding swift as a cat's as the lower-sea darkness clouded them. Did the fugitive turn blindly towards some vague undersea shape that itself moved, the Wanderer followed, unaware that more than once she was herself pursued for a short time in her turn.

No one knows why certain groups of these very young seal-cubs annually make this little migration to the Finmark coast in time to meet the capelin shoals, or why they stay as sunny week is followed by sunnier week till the cod shoals arrive. There must be reason in it, for in nature nothing happens without a purpose, but man, with still so much to learn, has not fathomed it.

The Wanderer and the painted cub frolicked in the flashing water, hardening sinews and muscles, and developing powers and instincts vital to the continuance of their lives. Once when she was swimming below the surface she saw sailing on the water a mallard duck.[1] As he dipped his head at some passing food she darted up within a foot of him, and with a wild squawk the duck shot into the air and went

[1] *Wild Wings*, by Frank Stuart (Gollancz, 1951).

screeching out of sight. The painted cub snapped a joyful recognition of the antic, and afterwards each of them looked for swimming birds to startle in this way whenever they could.

On a day of sheeting rain that fretted the sea surface into billions of tiny grooves there spread again among the joyous multitude a whisper calling them away. This time it came out of the north, to which, in truth and spirit, all the seals of our hemisphere belong. Though these children of the waves knew nothing of the place which called to them, they longed to go. Though there are no paths in the sea, a road beckoned them through the dissolving mists that wreathed the rollers, and singing through the hiss of the spray came a secret note, so insistent that it grew intolerable. Second-generation human emigrants know this imperative call as well as baby seals. Besides what the brain remembers, there is a memory in the blood which passes from generation to generation, a pulse which answers—"I will come!"

In the midst of gambolling among the breaking water the seal-babies stopped suddenly as if to listen. Hundreds of brown mermaid-eyes gazed north, yet where they looked was only an infinity of sea. They redoubled their boisterousness, jumped a wave, rolled on their backs. But presently there they were, staring north again, looking into each other's faces as if to seek some answer.

The Wanderer and the painted cub watched each other especially. They shared all their games, and constantly played at their tab-chasing. They had lost all memories of mothering, and to each the other seemed as inevitable a part of life as the sea that bore them or the air they breathed. Their friendship was as sexless as that. In their group were fifteen or twenty other cubs, all distinguishable from the hundreds of strangers about them. But these two had a special impulse to share a prank or seek each other in alarm.

Now, with the northern rain sweeping over the sea, hissing before a squalling wind, the two looked at each other for reassurance. With a dozen others they turned and began to swim into the rain, scores falling into place behind them. Again began that leisurely, unswerving migration rhythm. A backward sweep of one webbed foot, then the other, almost as if walking, while their bodies moved in a fast torpedo-glide that ate up the miles.

Presently the sea was covered by groups of seals as far as the eye could see. Sometimes they swam at high speed all close together, thrust forward, turned over and swam along just as fast and easily on their backs. There would be a jump of scores out of the water, then all would sweep on again at the journeying pace. Their numbers increased as they were joined by other sliding shoals, and presently a rough triangular formation emerged with a leader at its head. His movements were acknowledged; if he veered, the change communicated itself through all the swimming thousands, and if he paused in the great drive north, all waited.

Keeping always fairly near to the receding ice-edge, the seals first went north and then swung westward. The sun shone warm in a pale blue sky over a dark blue sea. The Wanderer had learned by now how to find plenty of crustacean food, and was growing sleek and comely with that special prettiness of all female young. Sometimes she sportively chased a little fish which flashed away, twisting and turning, gleaming like the painted cub's fascinating metal tab.

They passed a place where the distant sky was darkened by wheeling guillemots that screeched at the shoals of rival sea-fishers rolling along below. Then they sped in a great curve across the northern world towards Spitzbergen. And it was in the cold, glittering seas off those islands that the Wanderer swam carelessly into the shadow of death.

Attracted by deposits washed out from the distant land, drifts of tiny sea-creatures drove to and fro in the sea. The painted cub and his companion dashed among them, gorging themselves with food to a state of incautious somnolence.

Not old enough yet to set sentries in the usual seal fashion, they floated drowsily about, vaguely gesturing towards more of the illimitable swimming food-clouds. Presently several of the youngsters were asleep in the water. The Wanderer was one of them. Her flippers moved faintly, keeping her afloat. But she and two others drifted along with the current, oblivious of any sort of threat since so far they had never known danger except when on the ice.

The Wanderer woke abruptly and saw a shadow four times her own length shivering up from the deep towards her. Another seal-cub, still asleep, was treading water a yard away. As with her usual curiosity the Wanderer dived round the sleeper to investigate the oncoming apparition, there was a glimmer of chisel teeth in a curved mouth, and a gout of blood poured through the translucence of the sea. The sleeping cub screamed and bubbled as the Greenland shark's jaws cut it across the middle. With a twist of flukes the shark slewed its tremendous length. The Wanderer was scraped by the shingly roughness of a giant shoulder, then touched by a beating flipper of her dying playmate. As she twisted frantically to escape she saw for a second, staring glassily as it passed, the huge eye of the monster shark.

4. *Prisoner under Ice*

SOMERSAULTING sideways, the Wanderer went swift as a moving cloud-shadow through the dark water, every nerve stretched with fear. The shark, as big as a large boat, gripping the almost bisected seal in its jaws, followed. Generally sluggish and clumsy, these assassins of the seas can slide along at very high speed for a short, straight burst. The Wanderer, fast enough to overhaul a fish, had never before met a still faster pursuer in the element where few learn from experience, because a second chance is hardly ever given.

She felt the pursuer's disturbance almost on top of her. Had the shark not been gripping in its crescent mouth its first victim, one snap across the back would have shattered the Wanderer's backbone and pierced her organs with parallel rows of knife-sharp teeth. Some instinct forced her failing body into a backward somersault and dive. At once the great shadow disappeared, for these big sharks cannot turn as swiftly as that.

Still corkscrewing up and down, darting first to one side and then the other, pursued by nothing, the little seal rushed on in panic, imaging a sinewy, sea-wide presence, a broad and flat head, one great green eye, and saw-toothed jaws gaping several feet wide. Twisting and turning, casting terrified glances back, feeble from strain, a last violent effort took the fugitive to the surface.

Everything seemed just as before. All around her the young seals slept or sleepily idled in the water. They did not know that death had subtracted one from their number. The shark's rush had been silent. Only half a dozen cubs near by had heard the start of that mortal scream, doused under water almost before it began. For that is the shark's way of seizing the living food it must have. A creature is twitched under the water almost without a ripple, dragged deep, drowned, eaten. Then a new silent abduction is made from some other place fifty yards away, where no warning has been carried.

A dozen young seals vanished that sunny day. A herd of sharks was at work, quietly and efficiently killing and eating with no more emotion than the seals felt when they plunged into a shoal of passing shellfish or than a human animal experiences in eating a chicken.

While the great assembly of the seals sported and hunted for food and idled in and out of the sea in the Spitzbergen area during that sunny Arctic summer, their numbers diminished. Sharks accounted for some, other raiders for a few. Some died of old age. But there were more losses than this: some of them were vanishing in some unusual way.

The rest remained unsuspicious, playful, and happy. Drifting currents from the Arctic and the North Atlantic brought all sorts of sea creatures to that place, from monster whales to the tiny plankton on which the giants fed. The Wanderer grew familiar with them all.

The plankton alone constantly plunged her into a world of magic that surrounded her and drifted away again like undersea mist. Much of this plankton was so small that it could have escaped through the texture of the finest silk.

But sometimes the Wanderer swam among such astronomical billions that the waves were laid with a carpet of vivid green or rose.

In the lavish sea, though sometimes a single fish will spawn millions of eggs each year, on an average only a handful will reach maturity; all the rest for a few weeks wash to and fro as just one tiny contribution to the plankton world. Most of such floating wave-dust is invisible to the human eye; water filled with billions looks to us perfectly clear. But without plankton all the life in all the seas would starve. For those who do not eat plankton live on those who do.

Millions of square miles of the ocean floor are covered by deep oozes made up almost entirely of the coloured shells of minute dead plankton shapes, as exquisite as the multi-patterned crystals of snowflakes. Some are like gaily-coloured pointed crystals. Some seem like clusters of jewels adhering together. Some have hair-like radiations only comparable with the pricking glitter of stars on a frosty night.

Everywhere in the sea the composition and abundance of plankton changes as the seasons pass. At certain times of the year, especially in spring and early summer as the sun-light warms the water, there are outbursts of planktonic life resembling a discharge from millions of undersea volcanoes. There is no part of the oceans of the world where this satura-tion of plankton does not occur.

Richest of all beyond all credulity, the lovely jewels of sea-dust spread from sea-bottom to surface and from horizon to horizon at the edges of the Polar seas in those regions of melting ice where the seals go hunting.

Using carbon dioxide dissolved in the water, and trans-muting this by means of sunlight, the plankton live, grow, and reproduce. Without them the seas would change their nature, be empty, dead, perhaps eventually even poisonous. And this infinity exists in the water-pockets on one of the smallest of heavenly bodies, of which there are so many that perhaps they outnumber all the plankton in all the world's

oceans. And some of them are so large that our world would
lie on one as a particle of plankton lies on this; the orbit of
our earth around the sun could be placed inside one of the
greater stars.

The plankton often discoloured the climbing Spitzbergen
seas as the summer months passed slowly by, and hordes of
ocean life lived upon it. The whales came, and sounded like
sinking mountains, the seals plunged and played, and a
myriad other creatures fattened themselves there. Meanwhile other destroyers waited, man among them, till the
time was ripe to slaughter those the plankton fed.

All this while the Wanderer grew and exercised and
learned the thousand lessons of the sea. This colour in the
water meant food, that colour meant danger. This way of
the wind brought fog, and fog brought better hunting. That
shadow below was a shark from which instantly to flee. The
monster of shining metal, gliding on the surface towards
Advent Bay and attended by crowds of fulmar petrels, was
slow and harmless, and was in fact amusing to race round
with the painted cub. It was a tourist steamer from Oslo or
a collier rolling in to fetch a cargo from the island mines.

Glaucous gulls poised against the blue of the sky. Rotches,
black guillemots, ivory gulls, auks, and kittiwakes travelled
far seaward from the deafening bird-nurseries on the distant
cliffs. These birds were fishers too, but clumsy fishers who
offered little rivalry to the flitting seals, though they were
always good for a moment of fun when a seal surfaced beside
them and sent them screaming up the sky.

The bird-cliffs attracted the gaze of the Wanderer because
of their colour. Bird-droppings decaying with Arctic slowness had formed a sort of soil in which grew a carpet of moss
of most vivid green flecked with golden-yellow ranunculus,
brilliant saxifrages, and golden dancing poppies. In an
austere world of ice-white and sea-blue, other colours fasci-
nate of themselves, and the little grey cub would float for
hours in the sea watching them. Or she would lie with only

her nose above the swinging water as her fore-flippers held
her against a rock, staring while the spray shot in rainbows
over and over her head.

Out of the north-west one morning came a late summer
storm with rollers running high. The Wanderer felt the
climb and curl of the waves, to which she gave her body in
sensuous satisfaction. The kick of a webbed foot or a body-
swing perfectly co-ordinated took her flying up a hissing
crest, or gliding endlessly down into troughs that grew
deeper and deeper, and darker and darker green.

The biggest seas came three or four together, smooth and
round and mountainous upon each other's shoulders, each
curling its great white crest before it until one overwhelmed
another, and with a crash of sea-music sent columns of foam
spurting upward towards the fleeing sky. Then would follow
a long series of smaller seas, and then a group of slippery-
backed sea-monsters again.

In the giant lift and throw of those seas the seal-cubs felt
ecstasy. No swimming stroke could drive one forward at the
speed of this. To be flung like a stone, and yet be safe, to
ride a breaking sea faster than a bird in air, to become the
plaything of waves that could lift a ton of rock or smash a
mountain of ice, and yet be fondled, stroked, and petted by
them—this was exquisite. Passing and repassing each other,
seeing friends borne up, hurled down, they were like children
tossed between the hands of playful gods.

When the sun set great streamers of reflected colour glittered along the wave-tops for a hundred miles, touching
them with carmine. The breaking spray-clouds began to
shimmer with blue and violet, red and orange, yellow and
indigo and green, among which the seals leaped like fish.

The storm lasted three days and nights, and so much
exercise aroused hunger. The Wanderer was by this time
most familiar with the changing currents and their messages
of food and fear. Accompanied by the painted cub and two
other companions, she swam northward, searching for a

current that brought shoals of sweet little crustaceans with
it.

What began as a casual search for food developed into an
expedition. Scattered patches of shrimp-like life drew the
four youngsters farther and farther north. At first colonies
of other seals of all ages were passed. These thinned out and
ended, but still the adventurers swam north, playing elabo-
rate water-games or idling in the sun.

It was luxurious to lie stretched out on the ice again after
all the excitements of the summer. They dozed for hours,
woke blinking, scratched with a lazy flipper, then suddenly
hurled themselves into the freshly-cold water and dived deep
under the floes.

One evening the Wanderer chased a fish beneath the edge
of an ice-mass, diving down and down, wantonly playing
with the fleeting silver gleam. She was a splendid diver now,
and fearlessly chased her quarry ever lower under the ice.
They went in and out of caverns and round gloomy white
pinnacles in that inverted landscape till the light failed and
the pursuit continued by a sense of touch alone, her nose-
hairs guiding her racing through the ripples the fish had just
disturbed.

Seals have been caught in nets at a depth of nine hundred
feet. On at least one occasion a seal has been lowered during
an experiment to more than a thousand feet. No one knows
just how far down in the ocean they can go, but their whole
anatomy is designed for amazingly long periods of undersea
excursion. Though a normal fishing-dive does not usually
take more than about five minutes, seals have been known to
stay underneath for more than half an hour at a time.

The Wanderer grew so obsessed with the fish that she lost
all sense of direction. She zigzagged continually as her
quarry made desperate turns both to escape and to avoid the
undersea formations of the ice. Had she been more experienced she would have taken warning, because this ice-ceiling
over her head was different from anything that she had ever

seen before, and to the older animal the unknown always calls for care. But she was young.

Always previously, under the floes and bergs where she had played, there had been stretches of open water or breathing-holes. The ice-roof itself had been heavily fretted and broken. It was not so now. This ice was more or less flat, like a ceiling. It did not reach claws down. There was no break in it. It stretched solid, to right and left, in front, behind; and no light penetrated it.

The fish was of a kind on which older seals fed. The Wanderer was too young yet to eat such fish, but already instinct commanded her to pursue. As she obeyed that command, so the fish responded to the instinct of its kind to dive into this place where there would be safety from seal attacks, because they dared not follow.

Now, as the stored air in her blood began to thin and danger signals ran through her twisting body, the Wanderer glanced upward. The fish glided away unregarded. Her tactile senses told her there was a solid ice-ceiling over her head. The hunter had suddenly become the fugitive. She had trespassed into a place where the sea-law of kill or be killed decreed a fish sanctuary. Unless she could rapidly find a way of escape her own turn had come to die.

For this was what the Eskimos call a "seal-desert." Here the sea currents were too sluggish to break up the ice. It was frozen together in a far-reaching sheet above her, with never a crack or rift up which she could flee back to the air agonizingly needed to relieve her bursting lungs. Seals, too, can drown.

The Wanderer's movements began to grow feeble. Her head turned pitifully upward. She swam more and more slowly round and round in the lightless water under the black roof of ice. The purposeful shove and lovely streamlined, gliding movement failed. She began to roll very slowly over and over in a sluggish current, looking like a sodden and sinking driftwood log.

5. The Fiery Rain

THE undersea stream into which the drowning seal had
been carried rolled her slowly along in the dark. She
was bumped now and then against the roof of ice, and these
blows brought her back to consciousness for a few moments,
during which she struggled feebly. Then she became inert
again, head and tail drooping, only to be straightened by
some swirl of the current. Scarcely alive and quite unseeing,
her body was washed into a knife-like crevasse up which the
water was slowly flowing.

Some last instinct of self-preservation, some difference in
the swirl about her, sent messages to her limbs, and she beat
them faintly, trying to swim upward. Her pace increased.
A stab like the thrust of a knife passed through her body,
and she writhed and doubled in agony. Because she had
dived too deep and for too long, bubbles of nitrogen gas
were forming in her blood and she came too swiftly towards
the surface. Seals can be killed by such accidents as well as
men, but what might have slain another now saved the
Wanderer's life. In a piercing spasm her body whipped to
and fro; trapped in the ice-chimney, she was shot to the top
by these convulsions as if fired from a cannon.

Bursting into air, she lay on the water in the crevasse, bending and straightening by muscular reflex action. Then at last she was still, but for a faint motion of the flippers to keep her nose in air. She lay there for a long time, unconscious of her surroundings, unaware of life. She floated by that instinct which so often takes charge of wild things when all their natural endurance is at an end.

At last she stiffened and seemed to come alive. Paddling to the edge of the crevasse, she painfully climbed on to the solid ice. She dragged herself a few yards from the dangerous crack and then seemed to fall asleep.

All around her were huge pad-marks where, not five minutes earlier, a starving polar bear, followed sneakingly by a fox, had prowled through the snow. If now he had turned in his tracks the bear could have walked right up to the Wanderer. Instead, his belly groaning from hunger, he rambled farther and farther away. All the while she slept as if dead.

Awaking in the diffused light of the setting sun, she was immediately uneasy and began to look around for the sea. She lay among unbroken ice save for the dark crack up which she had been carried. She looked at the water lipping its edge and turned away. Some warning in her blood made her refuse to risk moving across that open white plain till night came to hide her from human or animal hunters. Perhaps the bear-tracks conveyed some threat. Later, in misty darkness under a shrill, rising wind, she lifted her head. Daytime observation had impressed upon her a need to turn south. Without any ability to reason, she yet began to move accurately and directly towards the only narrow lead of seawater within miles.

This creature never before out of sight of the swaying sea obeyed many new nerve-warnings. After nosing round she rejected all parts of the almost joined horizon circle where she had seen brighter sky reflecting unending ice-deserts, and began instead to hoist herself towards the single point where the sky had been darker over water. She hunched slowly past fantastic hummocks and wind-swept snowhills. Several times she made long detours for no reason that the eye could see. Some tremor in ice or air told her of peril—perhaps a crevasse treacherously snow-hidden in her path. When a pale moon flickered at times through racing clouds she slid from shadow to shadow in fast, clumsy, surprisingly-silent rushes, then lay resting and shrewdly observing all directions, a blot on black.

She set her fore-limbs on the snow and dragged along, leaving a spiral track. She had a long way to go, and often the surface was rough. The hair, and presently some of the skin, rubbed off her flippers, which deposited dark smears of blood in her track. She travelled at about a mile an hour, resting often.

At last she reached the sea's edge. A pause. One more careful look around for danger over water as well as ice. Then a splash—and she was in her own lovely element once more! A flying shadow now instead of the lump that had dragged itself along, she at once began to play.

Life-force surged back into her muscles, and strength from the swinging waters recharged every nerve. She shot out of a wave, dived again, raced along under the surface, twisted like a fish, all for delight at feeling the responses of the sea. Then she set off south along the narrow lead, urgently seeking her playmates, for seals are always uneasy when alone.

The lead opened to an ocean clashing with ice-blocks. The night gale whistled over them, and there was small, stinging snow in it, sliding almost horizontally along the wind and pitting the skin of the heaving sea.

The Wanderer swam steadily and fast. She needed food and rest, but most of all she craved the sight of her own kind. In that wilderness of waters, never seen before, she swam strongly in a certain direction, blindly making a correction where a current racing round a projecting ice-spit drove at several knots an hour across her path, allowing without

thought for the shove and sweep of the wind against the
surface waters. She was going she knew not where, but she
was going as if drawn by a magnet towards the main seal-
herd.

She swam on. Then, just as the moon was settling below
the waves, she dived abruptly from the rush of a white
monstrosity swimming down upon her. The sight of it was
terrifying in that feeble light. The apparition, twelve times
her own length, five feet thick, heavily and roughly armoured
in ice, was big enough to stave in the side of a steel ship. It
was all that was left of the trunk of a spruce fir, which had
endured enough adventures to fill a book as it rolled on its
resistless way.

It had seeded and grown to nearly a hundred and fifty
feet tall in a dense forest in Russia. Spring floods, draining
from more than a million square miles into the Yenisei river,
had uprooted it and borne it, leaping like a salmon, two
thousand miles down to the Kara Sea. There, butting its
way through the ice-blocks, it went rolling away past
Lonely Island out into the ocean. The Arctic Drift caught it,
and in sunlight and moonlight and through the darkness of
the six-month Polar night it had struggled on its way. Passing
near the North Pole, it had turned south until it plunged
four thousand miles from its birthplace, voyaging along the
desolate Spitzbergen shores. Sometimes it had been frozen
in ice as if for ever. Then the summer sun or the pile-driving
waves from a north-west gale had smashed it free again.

A touch from it would have broken the Wanderer's backbone like a twig. But she steered under it without alarm and
was surfacing on the other side when another and even bigger
white monster ploughed out of the mists down a twenty-foot
wave straight at her. She dived again as the two trunks
smashed together.

Swimming along six feet under, the seal looked up at a
school of trunks rushing over her head, flipped like match-
sticks this way and that by the mountainous seas. They were

stepping and sliding along in a crazy dance. One would stand on end, bow to the rest with drunken solemnity, then crash down, flinging up waterspouts to obliterate the moon. A hundred would step out together, shooting ice-splinters like a shower of daggers across the sky. Two would detach themselves, go bowing their hoary length across the wave-tops, dive, and come up still grotesquely paired. A dozen more would swirl like spokes of an eighty-foot wheel, spinning in a black whirlpool between the foaming seas.

Wheeling to the right with the current that drove these strange sea-creatures, the Wanderer began swimming with all her speed. She was racing them for pleasure, unable to let a challenge pass. But also she was escaping from danger. To trespass on the rolling dance-floor among these blind and frozen monsters performing their mysterious ritual beneath the sea-moon would be to invite death. To swim under them, except very deep, was to risk being struck as one of them up-ended. But the Wanderer did not want to dive—her time under the ice had left fear. So she sped along below and ahead of the tree-trunk herd, outstripping them so that their splashing and grinding and thudding died away behind.

Presently it was dawn. The brief autumn light spread miserly on a promontory where waves burst like a continuous barrage of natural artillery. The seal turned lightly in the current, staring at a miraculous sight.

On that shore, where no trees can grow more than two feet tall, was a madhouse of piled tree-trunks twenty to forty feet long. It looked like a timber-yard where an earthquake had taken place, flinging the logs in chaotic hills and spreads. They lay at all angles, many split or splintered. The great new mob the Wanderer had seen were coming—were almost here. Swept by gales far up the beach, here they would lie preserved by the intense cold, awaiting the gathering of their tribe from far Siberia, year by year.

To add a final touch of fantasy, leering at a drunken angle at the back and far above them all, was part of the oaken

keel and the wooden figurehead of an ancient ship. Cocked
rakishly against the Arctic skyscape, it glowered down bare-
breasted on the prostrate logs. For perhaps two centuries
already it had savoured their prone adoration. Each year
more came through the Arctic night, a thousand sacrifices
as the price of every spring.

Travelling south day by day, the Wanderer passed the
seal-colonies she had seen on her northern journey. Many of
the places were now deserted, and in others only a few sleek,
dog-like heads inquisitively broke the surface to watch her
pass. This hastened her pace, adding to the migration fever
already beginning to light little flares in her blood.

In one place a monster, emitting a steady noise and coming
at a speed that outmatched her own, began to make towards
her over the ice-lifting seas. It was a motor-boat, and a man
in it was lifting a rifle.

The Wanderer had never seen men before, or anything
like this fish-shaped thing coming so suddenly out of the sun.
She was alert, but also very curious.

Bang! went the rifle, and a whining past her ear cut a
vicious chip out of a wave. At that she dived without more
ado.

Still unaware of any acute peril, she circled deep in the
sea, staring up as the motor-boat drifted over her. The gun-
ner was swearing and peering down. He could not see her.
He thought he had shot her and that her body had sunk.
Presently the boat went roaring away.

Already the cold fingers of winter were reaching southward, choking down life. In the lanes among the old ice-
pack the Wanderer saw new ice starting to form. Sometimes
she swam in an oily-looking sea filled with ice-spicules, which
swiftly increased till big areas were covered with thin plastic
ice. Occasional drifts and flurries of snow added to its
thickness, and to the sludgy ice-slush between. As it became
thicker the ice lost its mobility, dulling the wave-movements
from underneath. Sometimes a wind smashed it up, but

each time it froze together faster than before. The sun rising for a brief time every day traversed a course always nearer the horizon, offering little warmth and hardly any light.

The Wanderer often crept on to new ice, dark and translucent where it was blown clear of snow. Its surface was rough and ridged, and rather sticky with salts thrown out as the water congealed. As the bay-ice formed it took the shape of hexagonal plates several inches across, which rolled and clashed against each other, turning up each other's edges. Presently they froze together with the pattern showing like a tiled floor.

These masses of ice drifted together and froze into floes, which broke up before the increasing gales and then were rejoined by frost. Everything glittered day and night, as if newly created. Sometimes ice would grow an inch or more in thickness in twenty-four hours. After the first few days of the floe's growth, snow usually covered the ice, weighing it deeper and deeper down. Sometimes the weight of this snow sank a floe to the water-line.

The coming of these heralds of winter made all the seals uneasy. The Wanderer, who had rejoined her herd, had not found the painted cub or the other two who had gone north with her. In a desultory way at times she searched for them.

Like the rest, she felt disturbed by the approach of the northern winter and by the steady loss of light. In them all pulsed a feeling calling them back along the tossing road that they had traversed from the White Sea, where the Wanderer and her contemporaries had been born half a long year ago.

Already detachments of from six to twenty swimmers were leaving. They swept along, playing and tossing, preferring to go in rough weather, which always challenged the travel impulse in their blood. Soon the parties of travellers increased to forty or fifty, then more.

Still the Wanderer did not go. She sought more urgently

for the painted cub and the group with whom she had come here. One day the three absentees returned. They were sleek and playful. They gambolled over and round the Wanderer, and she swam about them. Once more she and the painted cub played their game of pursuit of the bright tab. It was dulled now, but still glittered. They capered in the sea, raced up the rollers, plumbed the green depths.

One day, out of the cloudy sky there shot without warning a shower of hissing meteorites, countless millions of which invade earth's atmosphere every day. Before the seals could dive the sea boiled and spouted. There was a frightful whizzing noise, unendingly continued, and through the air fell balls of fire. One was large and glowing, the rest were like incandescent sparks. A splinter wide of the rest struck deep into a young seal with whom the painted cub was playing. Killed instantly, he sank down through the sea.

The other players dived like shadows. As they went they heard thundering detonations, and then a terrible and desolate noise like the roaring of unimaginable seas in echoing caves.

In that panic which strikes some animals when the sky puts forth strange phenomena the seals went flying towards the depths. The dead body of their playmate of a moment ago sank sluggishly after, as if following them down.

6. *Pursuit by Monsters*

THE shower of meteorites sent all the remaining seals flying south-eastward, like a cloud of minnows disturbed by a bather. Their alarm quickly faded, but the impulse to escape hurried them on. Soon the moving hundreds overtook the tail of the great tribal procession now swimming leisurely back along the way they had come.

From the waves as far as the eye could see a multitude of shining, dog-like heads glided along, looking with lovely and playful eyes, turning as if conversing, whirling into spontaneous frolic, diving and coming up to peer with ineffable surprise through a veil of sea-diamonded whiskers. Some swam upright, some on their backs, some turned somersaults in the leap and catch of the waves.

They looked like a tribe of mermaids—perhaps descendants of those mermaids Thomas Hilles and Robert Rayner saw sporting in this same spot round Henry Hudson's ship as it drove through the Barents Sea three hundred and fifty years ago.

The seals did not hurry across the world's northern curve in that perambulating migration which would eventually

D

bring those who lived and kept together to the White Sea again in springtime to start another year of ocean life. A chart of their route would have looked as tangled as a bit of discarded rope. Yet no part of it was patterned by chance.

They followed the mysterious fish roads of the ocean which lead not only to right and left, but also up and down, often to considerable depths. These fish roads are bordered in places by comparative fish deserts. The routes change with the seasons, and sometimes with the years. Countless shoals of creatures, great and tiny, traverse them, sometimes lingering, sometimes going swifter than the eye can follow.

Clouds of vegetable-eating inhabitants of the world of waters roll ceaselessly along the ways where vegetable plankton blossoms, and browse on it in their endless myriads. Pursuing them come all the hosts of hunters of the deep. Above move the menacing shadows of sea-bird hordes, and sometimes of spotting aircraft and fishing-fleets, as man seeks food, animal feeding-stuffs, corset-bones, seal-furs, hides, manure, oils, glue, and fine fish-skin leathers. From above, below, from every side, uncountable hostile eyes peer through the waters of all oceans, watching for any kind of movement, and wherever something moves death stabs at it. Most sea life exists by speed or cunning, preying on other victims until at last something reaches through the waters to strike it down.

Human animals fumble unceasingly in these crowded depths, trying to plot the fish roads. Scientists tabulate the growth-rate and seasonal migrations of the swimming billions, analyse the foods in their stomachs, mark and release fish by the ten thousand and pay rewards to those who trace their distant travels. The effects of moon changes, star attractions, sun-spots, are painstakingly noted.

In laboratories a-gleam with glass and steel, plants for the study of fishes have been set up. There, as only one of endless experiments under natural sea conditions, faint electrical charges imperceptible to human beings have been passed through great tanks of sea-water, and immediately whole

schools of certain fish rush from cathode to anode. Does this
mean that fish migrations follow faint electrical agitations
of the seas? Man does not know.

Whatever makes the sea-beings sweep along their plankton-
flowered roads, the seals obeyed it too. Across the Polar
ocean they romped their way. They hunted tiny, jumping
crawfish, and wove among young fish that looked like transparent snakes whose black spots of eyes alone showed clearly
against the water.

Once they played among jelly-fish—some like stars and
some like jugs, some like saucers and some like coloured bells
or wondrous flowers. Many were iridescent, some had
coloured lights in their foreheads which they could switch on
and off in the dimness. Some had whiskers, some fleshy
tails, some swam, some rolled, some seemed to climb for
ever up and down invisible stairs. Some rode on others'
backs, some lived in others' shells. Among them, now
ignoring the seals and now fleeing from them, moved bigger
fish of strange colours and every shape.

At other times the seals in their hundreds intruded into
strange rites of ocean's social life—its love-making and shelly
house-building, its games and its songs. Some denizens of
the waves have voices, and sometimes these voices are ridiculous and soprano, but sometimes they are deep and terrible.
Since sound is about fifteen times as audible under water as
in air, such noises may be striking. Men have made recordings showing that some fish cry out like aircraft-engines with
open throttles, while others produce drum-rolls twice as
loud as the noise of a busy city street and resembling in
rhythm an automatic drill biting into concrete. These
sounds are made by the action of vibratory muscles against
the fish's air-bladder.

Another fish can grunt louder than the noise of a passing
bus. Another utters shattering honks. Another emits steam-
boat-whistle blasts at regular half-second intervals. Some
cry for love and some for rage, some for hunger and some for

woe. Some are round and some are almost cubical. Some
look like black ropes trailing through the waters. Some have
eyes on top of their heads and some apparently have a sort
of sight in the nerves of their tails.

Among such creatures, as they dived on secret missions,
trekked in myriads to and fro, pursued or were pursued,
uttered their love-cries or floated vegetable-like in some
strange trance of exhaustion or gluttony, love-play or spawning, or twisted slower and slower in death, the seals gambolled,
hunting, sleeping, and watching.

Once, descending to the limit of their diving powers, the
pack of sea-dogs passed over the tops of submarine mountains
and saw other flocks of migrants travelling across undersea
passes. They found a patch of slowly-waving weed with
stems curling away a hundred yards long and splotched with
succulent coloured swellings. Round these wavered nations
of tiny shellfish—shrimps, and sea-spiders with deformities
of endless hair-like legs. On one mountaintop grew strange
spongy flowers of watery yellow and pink.

A school of deep-sea fish came shouldering their sturdy
way through the flowers, biting off the starfish rays, bolting
down the molluscs. A swaying jelly-fish caught one of the
raiders and began to consume it. Then a sightless monster,
drifting out of the depths, sent tremoring in its path through
the water an electric death-ray to paralyse victims that
might have dodged its clumsiness.

Half a dozen snaky shapes tore past the sponge-flower
grove and drew into their mouths fleeing minnows with ridged
and spiny backs. As they did so they were followed by a
torpedo-fish, which sucked into its jaws one after another.
Their own mouths were still busy chewing up their victims
as they slithered into a greater maw.

The seals sheered away and went flying up to the dark and
heaving surface under the Arctic night. Then an area a
mile square broke into sudden ghostly radiance. This faint,
far-spread island of light came and went, rollers seethed

over it, and it emerged again. It was the passing of a herring shoal, millions of fish close together. It shone like the body of Neptune turning in his floating sleep, and the dull and far-spread rustle of fish movement sounded like mighty breathing.

As the weeks passed the seal thousands rushed to and fro, observing everything, now playfully excited, now nervously in flight. Many were eaten; the rest swept impetuously on, as generations of past seals had done along this same route. They obeyed a call fiercer than hunger and stronger than fear. Irresistibly they drifted towards the White Sea.

If creatures gathered to slaughter them they swept aside in a great detour. If they were forced to flee back along their tracks it was only for a little while. In the end they came involuntarily round again. If the slaughterers still barred their advance at last in their thousands they would burst through the barrier of death itself. The undersea world would run red, and among the spreading streams the survivors would swim doggedly at top speed, twisting like hunted hares, breaking the blockade, and racing on their inevitable way faster and more urgently than before.

The Wanderer was growing stronger, more shapely, more skilled in the ways of ocean life. She had long ago shed the last remnants of her white puppy coat and become a soft and pretty grey. Her back was darkish, her underparts light. Soon after losing her wool coat she had begun to show a few indistinct darker spots. With each week these spots increased in number and deepened in colour. There was as yet hardly any difference in marking between her and the male cubs of her age. The painted cub was perhaps a little larger than she. Nor was there any consciousness of sex. They played as comrades, quarrelled amicably and briefly, sought each other if separated, but that was all. Only in one way did these two show a preference for each other, and that was in their favourite game in which she pursued the metal tab near his tail, and he tried to twist and face her.

Sometimes when they surfaced the heaving width of the Polar ocean was transmuted by bands of splendid colours as the Aurora Borealis flamed in yellow-green, with flutings of red, blue, and violet. The seals leapt curving from the curving waves, their shiny backs gleamed with the sky's colours, and as they dived again they seemed to drag threads and stains of red and yellow with them.

As the weeks went by the seals came more and more often to the surface, as though looking for something. Not seeing it, they rushed down the depths together, as if in petulant protest. But before long they were up again, turning anxiously this way and that, and looking at each other in doubt.

Once when they came up all together, driven by some common impulse, the thing they were waiting for happened. They began to dance in the sea.

Blacker flashes in the blackness, the young seals leapt as never before. Up and down they went in a sea-dance, helplessly quickening as they raced along. They had been born in a springtime of day-and-night; they had seen the unsetting sun at the height of an Arctic summer; and now for weeks their light had gone out and all their lives were dark. Somewhere out of their sight, behind the world, the light was starting to creep north again. They could feel it coming. Unable to stop themselves, they glided from the water, as if flying with wings, as if jumping to lessen by two or three feet the ninety-three million miles separating them from that by whose quickening heat alone they were able to live.

Exhausted by the sea-dance, dozens of the young seals climbed up on to a small ice-floe to rest. They left long trails as they crawled dripping through new snow and sprawled tiredly down. They lay there contentedly drowsing. Too young to post sentries, as older seals would have done, they savoured the blissfulness of childhood's fearless response that older animals never again enjoy. Too ignorant to be warned when the splashing of seals playing in near-by water stopped suddenly, they lay dreaming, scratching sometimes with an idle flipper, opening and shutting velvety dark brown eyes.

A horizontal black fish-tail, bigger than a seal's body, burst from a wave and hissed through the air. It smacked down on a young seal lying on the edge of the floe and shot it off into the water, which immediately swirled in a bubbling whirlpool. From that foaming water an immense rounded head rushed up, showing for a second two fins, like fallen ears, under its jowls. Gripping the broken seal in bristling jaws, it shook and crushed its victim, as a dog would a rat.

The other seals, terrified, dared not dive—this twenty-five-foot grampus was as swift and agile as themselves. It was raving with hunger; from the stomach of one such captured sea-monster thirteen dead porpoises and fourteen seals were extracted. In panic the fugitives began to scuffle towards the middle of the little floe.

The mountainous head vanished. A triangular dorsal fin, like a pirate's black sail, cut through the water, sank out of sight. Diving like a pike, the killer whale passed under the floe. Before the seals could move, its head, shooting up through the water like a battering-ram, hit the under part of the ice-patch, splitting it like glass and flinging the seals helplessly about. Then, bracing its body, the whale forced the cracking ice up, buckling, smashing, and tilting it at all angles, so that the victims were rolled off like marbles.

The Wanderer flung out her web-like hind-flippers in a dive. She cannoned against another seal, into which at that instant two rows of giants' teeth crunched sickeningly through hide, blubber, and bones. Then she went spinning sideways under the slimy curve of the whale's white belly.

For most of a year the Wanderer had lived in a world of playful friendship, with only fleeting moments of unremembered fear. An era in her life was closed by the horrible glimpse of the killer whale's head staring at her with her playmate in his jaws. Adulthood with all its fears had come.

In a panic such as she had never known the young seal pelted to and fro through the waters. Sometimes others of her friends shot across her path. The seas roared with the drumming of pursuit. Shadows came at her from every side. For killer whales sometimes hunt in packs, and can manœuvre with intelligence and skill. They do not simply hurl their dreadful bulk blindly at their victims. They surround and methodically collect them, sometimes harrying them into exhaustion in ferocious play.

They can and do maintain pursuit of a group of seals for days, and even weeks, across the northern seas. If there is a pack-ice promontory ahead then they will deliberately drive the fugitives against it until there is no escape. If the weary victims try to rest on a floe the whales will break the floe. Even huge Greenland sharks and giant squids flee—if they have time—before the savagery of the killers' plunging approach. If this sea monster has a natural enemy, man does not know of it. Here is something that nothing else will attack, that rolls through the seas, killing and maiming, but is itself irresistible.

The Wanderer fled. For a while she saw many other seals like moving shadows about her. Then a monstrous thing swam down among them, broke and tore them, and stained the sea with their blood. Later she was alone, but still the shadows pursued, seeming to gambol about her, to head her off, and then to drive her on again.

She dared not stop to eat. Seals can go for weeks without food, but this race for life through unknown seas, the loneliness, and the mountainous rushes of the whales brought her nearly to collapse.

How long the death-hunt lasted, how long afterwards she continued to flee when none pursued, the Wanderer had no means of understanding. At last, her feeble limbs refusing any longer to obey her will, she drifted slowly to the surface. She was emaciated, overborne, her big brown eyes were glazed and sunken in their furry sockets. In her scarcely

breathing body that sense of direction which all animals have until prolonged panic drives it out of them was broken, as a mainspring might be broken.

She was lost.

7. *Place of the Strangers*

ALONG the edge of the Barents Sea the Wanderer fled westward in panic. Solitary, and far from her tribe, she was troubled continuously by an instinct whose directive force had been blinded by inexperience and terror. Her blood stirred in her because she should have been making her way with the others towards the White Sea. Instead, she hurried on through strange seas in the wrong direction, still continuing along the westward line of her flight.

On the day that she lost the sense of being pursued she was almost at the limit of her endurance of hunger. Plunging like a stone down through the green seas she searched frantically for the crustaceans to which she had been accustomed. There was none here. As she swirled about, hounded by the gripe in her belly, a school of small fish swerved out of her path. Instinct turned her quick as a cat, and she snapped one of them across the back, cutting it in two. She swallowed its head, then went twisting after the rest as it slowly sank, and gulped it down.

The beating slither of it in her jaws was good, and she swam sideways after the others. The harp seal is the cleverest of all the swimmers of the seas. In a moment she was among the fish again, bit another in half, and snatched up the falling head after bolting the tail. Twisting and turning in that pale green world, and attaining new feline graces of movement in pursuit, she passed a significant stage in growth. The playful creature that had lived so far on little crustaceans now became, as a yearling, of necessity a killer of fish.

The rapid processes of seal digestion turned the new food into energy and warmth. She felt her heart beat rapidly. She struck out with her limbs and chased passing fish to taste again and again that Luciferian tremor of power, growing with what it feeds upon, that all creatures seem to enjoy when causing fear.

She was alone when she discovered this, so she had unlimited leisure to indulge it, instead of being busy with the communal activities of her age-group. She developed an inordinate appetite for hunting fish, whether to kill, or to taste the dark pleasure of their fear. And those who say that wild things do not do this can have observed but few of them.

As with us all, the power to cause terror induced and sharpened her own capacity to suffer it. Hitherto she had been innocently oblivious of danger, or almost instantly forgetful of it. Now, by causing fear, she was constantly aware of it.

As she swam westward through the seas, she often fled at the top of her speed and with a thumping heart when nothing pursued her. This new suspiciousness may sometimes have saved her life in her solitary condition with no one to aid her watchfulness; it is a universal penalty that life exacts from all who reach adulthood.

One day when the Wanderer came to the surface a wonderful thing was happening. The long, sunless Polar night was coloured by a narrow reddish beam of light at the horizon. What she saw was no more than a mirage. The sun was still below the sea, but its reflection had come twenty-four hours before it could appear. From that time, an hour or two at first, but swiftly growing, day returned.

Swimming doggedly on, the Wanderer presently approached the area of Jan Mayen Island. Once she suffered a start from some dolphins, who were much bigger than herself, black above and white below, like little killer whales. They shot past her without a glance. All leapt together, as though to clear some invisible ice-block, then went plunging in a beaked dive under the crest of a wave, each leaving a glittering track of bluish-green. Flying in time with them came a formation of kittiwakes, with white breasts and pearl-grey backs. They dipped now and then after small fish that fled from the dolphin hunters, then glided stiffly on motionless wings, keeping effortless time with their partners below.

An assembly of thousands of little auks rode dipping and balancing like a regatta on the sea. Mountains of water slid unhurryingly from horizon to horizon. Above a single fulmar sailed, gliding smoothly over the hill-curves of the waves, down into a hollow, then up on noiseless wingbeats to the high crests, intently watching the water that raced by below.

The nights were dark and cold, but the sun gathered strength day by day. The air temperature was two or three degrees below freezing still, even at midday, and the water refreshingly cold. There was a lot of floating ice, and the Wanderer often hauled herself out on to a floe to rest and laze in the sunshine. She had forgotten that once she was with a tribe of other seals. A solitary existence was all she remembered, though at times she lifted her head and grunted discontentedly, as if she missed something. Then some new thing would rouse her curiosity, and she would swim off to explore it as happy as she had ever been.

One midnight, as the stars faded, a glorious red glow overspread the northern world. Next morning a mirage showed a school of ice-blocks floating apparently in the sky.

Later there was a strange appearance of open water where the pack-ice stood solid and forbidding. Clouds gathered heavily from hour to hour.

That night, as the Wanderer lay on an ice-floe, she lifted her head sharply and looked around. A distant whisper of sound had come to her, the first seal-sound she had heard since being separated from her tribe. She had, in fact, not heard this imperative *maa*-ing since she herself was a white-coat pup an unrememberable time ago. Yet the tiny bleat-ing, hardly more than a nerve tremor, coming from miles away on the night wind, set quivering in maternal anticipa-tion some hidden string of her virginity. There was a sudden *plop*, and she was beating powerfully through the water in the direction from which the call had come.

She surfaced once or twice to listen again for that chorus of feeble voices. It grew louder and nearer. Quivering with excitement, she came suddenly to a narrow passage in the ice, leading into a lagoon. Some trick of the current caused the sea to run quickly there, and a dozen seals were playing in its sliding rush, treading water with half their bodies above the streaked surface, then tossing their hind-flippers in gamin gestures to the winking moon.

As the Wanderer swam in, they stopped as if a current of natural electricity motivating them had been switched off. In sudden terror she stopped too.

They were harp seals of her own kind—she could see the black saddle-marks on their sides. But they were slightly smaller, faintly different, foreign. She hesitated, ready to turn and flee. But as they lay unnaturally still in the swift current watching her there rose from right beside her the baby chorus of the whitecoats, squalling as they crawled about looking for milk and warmth.

She gave a single paddle-stroke that sent her gliding slowly on. The dark shapes crowding across her way did not move. With a strong kick she dived under them and on down beneath the ice-floes at their backs. No knowledge guided her. She simply obeyed a command in her brain, not knowing why.

As if this had happened before, she immediately found a hole in the ice over her head, and snaked herself into it and upward. Where she entered it the hole was wide, but it narrowed funnel-wise to barely shoulder-width, stoppered by a thickish skin of ice. Floating upright in the hole, she began to scrape powerfully with her nailed fore-limbs. She blew out from her lungs the small quantity of remaining air, which heated the ice while she drove with her hind flipper-feet to turn herself like a twisting drill and force her weight upward. The ice-skin cracked. She rested her fore-limbs on the top edge and looked swiftly round for danger, then heaved herself out on to the ice. Immediately several dim white shapes lolloped towards her, bleating anxiously.

Harp seals do not make breathing-holes in ice, but when cubbing they cut passage-holes to allow access to, and escape from, their young without going over the distant edge of a floe. Such holes, sometimes found in floes more than three feet thick, are bored out from beneath when the ice covering that particular place is thin and newly formed. The Wanderer later saw seal-mothers going up and down frequently every day, several seals using one hole in common. An ice-skin formed and re-formed, but was scratched away from below, and ice-splinters dragged up each time eventually formed a small crater round the top of the hole.

It was above such a hole that she now stood. Though she had never used one before, she had dived and found one, and scratched her way up it, guided by an intelligence inherited from seal-mothers who had evolved such processes through millions of years.

Most of the snowy-white pups looked desolately at her and wailed. One, with childhood's fearlessness of strangers, bunted urgently at her side. She shrank at this alien nearness, and half-heartedly snaked round and knocked it away. It bawled, and she stood poised, staring bewildered at it.

With a rush its mother floundered out of the hole, and her teeth glimmered like a spitting cat as her cub flung itself to her, murmuring. The Wanderer slithered away, an apologetic grey yearling again in the presence of jealous maternity. There were cubs all round her, crawling and beseeching. But she was frightened of them now. With a sidelong rush she went across the floe, and flopped into the sea. Its cool caress received her as it always did, unquestioning and safe.

Her sense of the strangeness and faint hostility of the harp-seal tribe to which she had come soon diminished. Yet she behaved as if on sufferance. If one of them made a move towards her, instead of playfully replying she turned uneasily away. If she and another poised equidistant from a fish or a tasty mouthful of shrimps, she slipped aside as if after something else.

Where the seals crowded so closely as to make an almost solid covering on the sunny ice, she paddled quietly along the floe-edge until she could climb on to it at a less populous place. She used the ice-holes, but only when no other seal was near. Sometimes she played timidly in the sea at the edge of a group of leaping strangers, nervously seeking their community, but not daring to intrude.

Day after day she cautiously explored the life of the breeding-lair. On the floating floes hundreds of small woolly cubs crawled about, uttering their futile cries, looking for their mothers, or playing with baby ferocity with bits of snow. In the open water the adults swam and gambolled and kept watch. They made constant trips to the young ones, and lay peacefully blinking while a cub tugged and floundered in wriggling gluttony. Occasionally the mother would curve her graceful body and suckle softly at another of her own teats.

All the while, in a slow and steady movement of the main Arctic current, the ice-ships drifted along the edge of the ice-pack. The floes swayed almost imperceptibly up and down as they sailed past a snow-hummocked coast, a nursery fleet of twinkling white crowded with furry babies on a voyage as mysterious and predestined as a dream.

The cubs, born lean, rapidly grew as round as snowballs from the creamy milk they drank, while the once-fat mothers became lean and fretful. The cubs were suckled several times in twenty-four hours, and shrieked urgently between feeds, especially at nights.

During this stay with the tribe near Jan Mayen Island the Wanderer learnt one more necessary lesson of her existence. Though the seals often slept on the ice, she noticed that they stirred in their sleep at intervals of a few minutes, lifted their heads, and looked briefly round about. They then lay down to sleep again, if, indeed, they woke at all during the ritual performance of this instinctive act.

If anything alarming or unusual met that blindly searching gaze, or if there was a strange sound in a cub's wail or in the grunt of a distant adult, consciousness leapt into the glazed eyes, and the flabby body tensed. Though she had never done this, the Wanderer copied it now, at first haltingly, waking with terrified starts, but soon habitually and hypnotically like the rest, never properly waking unless something was amiss.

After her great sea journey she lay somnolently on the ice, sometimes for two or three days and nights together. The snow under her did not melt as it would have done beneath any land animal, from the escape of body heat; the blubber layer under her skin insulated her hot blood from the ice-chill and shut in all the natural heat made by her own body.

On one occasion she was staring round in sleep-entranced sentry-go when her eyes focused on a distant black spot in the sky, and she instantly awoke. As the thing came flying at her on stiffly-outstretched wings, roaring terribly, she slipped down an ice-hole under the floe. The aircraft passed low overhead, the two men in it noting the position and estimating the size of the breeding colony. Then it turned back towards the distant sealing-ship that had sent it out to spot seal-nurseries ready for a mass killing.

The weather changed that night. The long spell of sun-shine ended, and a north-west gale brought ice hurrying and jostling round the edge of the pack. The sealing-ship's powerful engines and reinforced steel hull barely saved her. The big screw steamer ceased to be a hunter and became a victim, twisting in its attempts to escape. The wind, the sea-hills, and the hunting-pack of ice-rafts chased it south.

When the storm was over the sea continued to run high. The thin flakes of ice broken off by its violence froze together in round pieces a foot across, looking like hundreds of sea-lilies floating. Quickly these joined each other and froze into solid masses resembling sections of greenish-grey marbled floor.

The Wanderer took trips by herself, searching for food, which she never felt bold enough to take when there were many of the strangers near it. She explored for a good dis-tance, swimming swiftly along the edge of the great white promontory of ice—pointing eastward—that the drift of the Polar current forms each spring north-east of Jan Mayen. She passed other harp-seal nurseries extending as far as the eye could see. They were populated with creatures like herself, yet secretly different, and because of this difference she remained restless and unhappy.

Accidentally separated from the seal-tribe that travels to and fro between the Spitzbergen area and the White Sea, she had now fallen in with another harp-seal nation which sweeps between the north-east Greenland sea and Jan Mayen, some going as far as Iceland. A little smaller-built than the White Sea tribe, they tolerated her with indifference, perhaps because harp-seal individuals vary so much in size and markings that a stranger is not conspicuous. Yet they seemed to sense that she was from some other place, and they did not fully accept her.

It made her constantly uneasy, though now she had no

E

active memory of her own people. One night she dreamed
of the painted cub, seeming to dive round him chasing his
strange extra eye in delighted reunion. Her body jerked
with swimming movements, and she woke and searched
about, not knowing why, among the coldness of the strangers.

8. The White Giants

BEFORE the picture in her mind faded she had plunged off
the floe into the water and swum eagerly questing out
through the channel into the sea. As the water soothed past
her all uneasiness was washed away. She went on, sculling
along with graceful, easy strokes, covering a mile in three
minutes. Then she turned upside down, and swam along just
as lithe and fast, watching the water below for signs of food.

The sea suddenly darkened. She righted herself, and
found on glancing about that its usual pale, almost colourless translucence had changed to a vivid grass green. Countless billions of floating diatoms had stained several acres of
the Arctic sea with gelatinous plankton. It was as if some
deity, in haste to colour the land vegetation before the fleeting
Polar summer passed, had spilled in the water a palette of
verdant green.

Always excited to playfulness by anything new and strange,
the Wanderer began to cavort along in the bright green wash.
Leaping out and diving back into it, tearing at full speed
along the surface with a little, sleek wake V-ing away, her
head cut a path across this sunlit meadow of the sea.

Suddenly she scrambled on to a block of green ice. As it swung this way and that from the violence of her landing, flashing like an emerald heliograph, she sprawled precariously, as though challenging this icy playmate to toss her back into the water.

It could—it did! But in a moment she was riding on its back again—only to be slid promptly off once more, clutching with all her nails. Fast as a fish she drew two circles round it in the sea, then mounted with a rush and hung triumphant there. It rocked more and more slowly beneath her sprawling and graceful embrace.

This was no morning for idleness, and as soon as the emerald block was submissive to her will she flung it rocking away from her in a plunging dive. Down, down she went— saw a fish dart and caught it before it could turn. Then up, carrying it, a delighted splash as her head burst into the sunshine, and now a new game altogether, trying to mount the ice-block without losing the fish gripped in her jaws. But this was easy! With the beautiful swiftness of wild things, she had already mastered the balance needed. So she lay there eating her fish in the warmth of the sun, blinking, registering automatically in her memory a desire to hunt fish when she met coloured patches in the sea. The fish, plankton-fed, gather in such places; Nature was instilling through a game one of her secrets of the wild.

These areas of vivid Arctic water—caused by deeper layers of sea, containing infinities of diatoms, steadily rising to replace surface water that is cooled by melting ice and then sinking—attract a chain of creatures. Tiny ones come to eat the plankton; bigger ones arrive to eat the tiny ones, and then are themselves eaten, as they pause to eat, by others who pursue them.

Sometimes plankton colours ice-floes below water-level as red as if they were smeared with blood. Sometimes such ice is stained a bright yellow. Patches of water, varying in size from a few yards across to a square mile, may turn brown or green, red or yellow. The vertical circulation of the ocean constantly replaces at the surface those substances without which innumerable species of animal life, ranging in size from the shrimp to the whale, would starve and vanish.

Refreshed by the fish she had eaten, the Wanderer darted away through the green sea. She had seen something toss on the crest of a distant wave. She overtook it, bunted it gently with her nose, and played with it for a moment or two. Once she caught it between her fore-flippers and sat up in the water with it.

What she had found was a marbled, grey-black lump of ambergris, released from the body of a living whale, a concretion around the horny beaks of squids that the whale had eaten and could not properly digest. The seal swiftly tired of this greasy companion, and tossed it away. It was a fifty-pound lump that in the past would have fetched its weight in gold. Even to-day such stuff is valuable: as a basis for perfumery in the Western world, and as a cookery flavouring in the East. To the seal it was not edible; it could not play as the ice-block did; there were other things in the sea that morning more precious and exciting than it.

She passed into a sunny bay of ice, where the green water stained the pack-edge. In such water, baby seals would only have to open their mouths to find quantities of tiny crustaceans floating in. No seals had yet reached this coloured area, but the nursery floes, with their milk-drinking burdens, were steadily drifting this way.

A natural miracle was happening as the vertical currents brought up unending supplies of baby-food to meet the approaching infants who must somehow learn to eat. Seals always choose as nurseries groups of ice-floes which will— by the time the young are born and old enough to need such food—have drifted, often at the rate of eight miles a day, to a suitable feeding area. But it is not till four or five weeks after birth that the cub, which stops taking milk at about two weeks old, begins to look for its own food. The mother

seal has then long deserted her offspring. She cannot possibly know where the breeding-floes, drifting along in the
Arctic currents, will be in a month's time. Yet the timing is
always perfect. When the newly swimming cubs are ready
for it their food is there—floes and plankton have met.

The Wanderer was still too young to care about cubs and
their problems. Swimming far ahead of the seal-horde she
played in the green waves, passing sunny hours. She was
treading water, resting her fore-flippers lightly on the edge
of a floe and staring dreamily when she saw across the floe
on the distant ice-pack three white shapes. She stiffened in
alarm.

In front, rolling noiselessly, silkily along, was a bear, five
times the weight of a man. Behind her, in perfect silent
imitation, drifted a cub of about a year old. And behind
the cub—at a respectful distance, but obviously part of the
cortège—sidled, like a brownish shadow, an Arctic fox.

They were a long way away, and the Wanderer had no
instant fear of them. They kept their distance, and she was
in her own element, ever ready to engulf her. The white
giants, with their sneaking courtier, passed with an undulating action out of sight behind a range of snowy hummocks,
the same colour as themselves. They were walking purpose-
fully towards the seal-nursery. But since the Wanderer
could not anticipate distant danger, she was simply relieved
to see them go away from her.

She had never before seen either a bear or a fox. Yet
some warning discharge from the glands made her glide
uneasily off the floe and begin to swim quickly back the way
she had come. The fun had suddenly faded from the green
sea and the joy from the sunlight. She hurried along under
water, coming up now and then with only nose and eyes
above the surface to look swiftly round before sinking once
more.

At the nursery everything was as usual. Cubs crawled
about the floes, while their mothers and fathers played or

idled in the sea. It was comforting, it was peaceful. The
Wanderer hauled herself on to the ice and prepared to sleep.
Still she was uneasy—every minute, at first, she would lift
her head and gaze about, then nervously sleep again.

A few yards away lay a yearling the Wanderer had come
to recognize, because of a way in which he differed from
her and all his kind. He slept, never lifting a head to look,
only stirring very faintly and listening. It was the same in
the water; whether he hunted fish or took part in games, he
never seemed to look, but only to listen. By listening he
could tell, in flashing water-play, what to do as another seal
dived at him at a speed of thirty feet a second. There was
another peculiarity too. He had made two or three attempts
to play with the Wanderer. The others coolly accepted her,
but she was kept apart by them. Whether they played, fed,
or rested, it was as if they did not see her. Because this one
cub showed no aversion to her, she slept near him when she
could.

She saw him now lift his head more sharply than usual
and listen. He was alarmed. Not for a long time did he sink
down to rest again. The white bear and her cub, with the
fox a dozen yards behind them, were watching the floe!
A sound inaudible to all the other seals had been felt rather
than heard by this one—the infinitesimal sound of the bear's
head moving as she spied with dreadful caution round a
hummock.

A lane of water ten yards broad separated her from the
floe with its burden of seals. The old mother bear eyed them,
marking them down. From her hummock to the sea-edge
was twice her own giant length, and there was no possible
cover. She snarled soundlessly back at her big, gangling
cub and at the grizzled fox, who sank down on his belly with
a sort of deprecatory, bloody grin. Deliberately waiting till
all the adult seals together were sleeping with heads down,
the white giant crept forward. The other two lay as if
dead.

The bear's white colour made her indistinguishable to the
seals' vague out-of-water sight. Yet every time a seal moved
she froze motionless as a snow-heap and hid her black nose
with a white paw. Nose and eyes alone betray a hunting
bear against a white background, and in ages of evolution
bears have learned this trick to make themselves almost
invisible. There was a terrifying patience about her. It was
as if she knew she need not hurry, the end was so sure.
When a seal moved she lay still and covered. When all were
quiet she drifted forward on her belly as noiseless as a cloud.

She reached the sea's edge and paused. Then her eight-
hundred-pound hugeness seemed to dissolve in the water like
a melting heap of salt, without a ripple where she went down.

The sun shone, the white-coated baby seals lolloped about.
Adult seals popped up first here and then there, listened and
looked, and sank down again to sleep. The sea was empty.
But anyone peering down through the clear water might
have seen a white shadow pass down underneath the ice-floe.
Presently it emerged on the other side, near where the
Wanderer lay. A black nose broke the surface like a bubble,
the bear trusting for guidance to her amazing sense of smell
instead of to her indifferent sight. The shining black thing
sank under the surface as the Wanderer lifted her head in a
routine alert. She settled again.

A paw felt along the edge of the floe, gripped it with
dagger-like nails, and the whole giant shape surfaced without
a sound and began to rise on to the floe-edge as lightly as in
a nightmare.

It was the strange yearling who heard something in his
sleep and flashed into the water, and there were half a dozen
almost simultaneous adult-seal splashes as the bear, with one
frightful cat-like bound that sent water spouting, sprang on
to the ice and struck at the Wanderer's back. But she was
already hurtling sideways, and the wind of its passing boomed
in her ear as that sledge-hammer paw missed her by an inch
and scored deeply into the steely ice.

Already the bear-cub and the fox were swimming towards
the floe. The Wanderer and the others, scattering like a
school of minnows, avoided them and plunged away into
the depths of the sea.

With a loose-limbed leap the old bear reached a whitecoat
cub too young to understand fear, and broke its back with
a single blow. Turning, she bit another in the neck. Her
cub and the fox were scrambling on to the floe. The fox sat
down on the edge, his tongue red and lolling, waiting till
his betters were satisfied. But the young bear rushed in to
join the slaughter.

The mother bear tossed a seal-cub into the air and caught
it in her mouth, as a cat will do with a mouse. Then her
giant teeth crunched through it. At the edge of the floe a
seal-baby, vaguely alarmed, whimpered irritably and kept
looking doubtfully at the wash of the waves and then drawing back. The young bear rolled silkily that way while
the fox sidled up to the body it had abandoned after eating most of the blubber and blood. The bear-cub swung
round, and the fox shrank back. Then a new white baby
was seized and slaughtered while the fox slunk forward
again.

These foxes follow bears across the drift-ice hundreds of
miles from land, and feast on the flesh they leave. During
the Arctic summer bears sleep by day when they can, and
move about mainly by night when their poor sight does not
matter and their extraordinary powers of scent give them
advantages. But they will readily hunt by day if driven by
hunger, and in a seal-colony they slaughter everything they
can reach, far beyond what they need.

For two days the Wanderer dared not return to the floe,
and in this time instinct kept her near the strange yearling
whose hearing had saved her life. He seemed pleased at her
nearness, and hunted with her or played round her in the
water. On the second day, towards evening, the two of them
approached the floe.

It looked just as before. Yet the yearling obstinately refused to approach it. They paddled to and fro, looking at it from all angles. It seemed deserted. There were no white-coat cubs on it, no older seals, and there seemed now to be no bears. Still they did not go near it.

Then something moved like a soft brownish plume. It looked quite innocent, it had the shape of no possible hunter —just a slow-moving plume somehow attached to a little heap of snow. The strange cub would not go near, but the Wanderer gazed more and more and itched with curiosity. She swam nearer, then turned and raced away. She swam nearer still. The brown thing moved in such a fascinating way; she had never seen anything like it. It was not near the edge, so landing would be necessary to examine it more closely.

The movement came from down-wind of her, so she could smell nothing alarming. She stared all around, but there seemed to be no threat anywhere. The plume slowly moved. It was too much! With her fore-flippers on the edge she looked cautiously right round once again. Then she began to climb on to the floe.

The fox, which had often traded on other animals' curiosity thus to decoy them into reach of its leader, the old bear, lay hidden behind the snow, occasionally moving its tail. It shivered and slavered with desire as it played this old fox trick, though it was fully gorged already. The two bears, also heavy with food, crouched concealed behind a hummock a few yards away.

Without warning, the young bear bounded clumsily at the half-landed seal, missing her by yards as she slid terrified back into the sea. The fox snarled and snapped at the empty air, but the mother bear leapt past her cub and dived. It instantly followed.

White and monstrous, the two came curving down through the water at the Wanderer's tail. They could not match a seal's swiftness unless, as now, they leapt after it off a floe-edge and so used the impetus of their weight to overtake the victim in a straight dive.

The Wanderer felt the water shake as the pursuers plummeted after her, and instead of doubling away she tried in panic to race them down through the swiftly darkening depths.

9. A New Fur Coat

THE young seal plunged down into a water-darkness more forbidding than any she had known. With ears and nostrils tightly shut and lungs emptied of air, living on oxygen stored in her blood, she swam deeper and deeper. All the time the large nerves at the base of the hairs on her nose and brows registered the turbulences that pursued her, and signalled desperate demands to flagging muscles for more speed. In that place of intense pressure she glided about till feebleness and sudden blindness ended the deepest dive she had ever taken.

Her lungs had been forced into collapse by the pressure of other internal organs, and the air in her windpipe and lung-linings had thickened the tissues there. She seemed to shrink into herself, turn over, and stop moving. Then she began to rise like a released bubble.

Somewhere during the dive the bears had lost her. As she surfaced she felt again those pains from the nitrogen bubbles in her blood that she had experienced once before, when she was trapped under the ice. She drifted about convulsively bending and straightening. If an enemy had come then she

could not have moved an inch to save herself. Her glazed
eyes vaguely mirrored the forms of the white giants walking
sulkily away over distant ice, but her body made no response.
They were up-wind of her, or they would have smelt and
killed her within a minute of her surfacing.

With the wonderful quickness to recover which wild things
possess, she took several deep breaths that stopped her pains
and quickened her heartbeats back to normal. Having in
the human sense no constructive memory, her fears faded.
But the instinct that preserves wild things prevented her
from returning to the floe after this second attack, though
she had already forgotten the cause of the attack and thought
the floe was really empty now. If she met it in recognizable
shape a year or five years later she would not land on it.

She began to search the water leads for the dispersed seal-
colony and for the yearling with whom she was growing
friendly. Swimming companionably between the familiar
little ice-islands, she came at last upon some of the seal-
mothers whose babies had been eaten by the bears.

They were resting on a floe a mile away from the place
of their loss, a little group of a dozen with no males or cubs
near them. They lay very quietly, and they must have been
out of the water for some time, for their faces were wet with
the copious tears seals shed. They had no appearance of
sorrow or remembrance, yet at times one would touch
another timidly with a fore-flipper. Perhaps it was some
automatic action, a blind repetition of the movement made
so often to caress a baby now inexplicably vanished. There
they lay, silent and unplayful, in unmeaning tears, making
their futile gestures of love.

A hundred yards away some yearlings were playing in the
sunny water, and among them was the stranger who listened. When the Wanderer swam up behind him, pretend-
ing to bite him, he seemed delighted, recognizing her by a
distinction of her sinuous swiftness through the water, as
we might recognize a friend by a particular footfall behind

us. He dived away and spun beneath and up beside her in a water-wavering curve of beauty.

In a leisurely way the seal-host was already preparing to disperse. There was no migration yet, but groups of a score or so drifted along the pack-ice edge, apparently independently, exploring floating food-patches or hunting fish-shoals, yet steadily separating into two main companies. The larger body verged slowly towards the north-west, and the other group, to which the Wanderer was attached, began making a preparatory survey more southward.

Now, when everything seemed happy and peaceful and when her friendly spirit received daily comfort by recognition from another creature of her own age, a new disturbance crept into the Wanderer's life. She found that her fur was coming to pieces.

The beautiful glossy grey coat speckled with handsome darker spots was turning rusty brown and harsh. The collar that had been so rich around her neck was shedding hair attached to tiny crusts of dark and horny skin. She was immediately uneasy, not knowing why.

All gregarious creatures sharply notice differences in themselves or each other. Strangeness is always resented under that merciless law of the herds and flocks whereby all the injured and diseased are cast out so as not to infect or delay the rest. The middle nation of the harp seals experiences most of its physical reactions a little later in the year than the White Sea tribe. Because of this their coats still shone in the sun. Immediately they sensed the change in the Wanderer they froze into a new and harsher estrangement.

Only her yearling friend permitted her to come near. She sought him out with pitiful eagerness, showing a kind of sad and humble anxiety always to be near him as the condition of her coat steadily deteriorated. At first he seemed pleased and responsive. Then he gradually grew hostile, snapping at her to drive her off.

Frightened by the daily increasing enmity, the Wanderer

climbed on to a big ice-floe and lay there in the hot sunshine.
She scratched miserably at the top of her head, then reached
round to the middle of her back, where more patches of hair
from her coat were loosening and tickling and coming away.
Sometimes, with the back of her five-fingered hand-like
flipper, she would wipe her nose, then rub at the tears that
streamed continually from her eyes.

She lay there day after day and night after night, abandoned and alone. Her special playmate had completely
deserted her. She could see him racing with the others in
the sea, but she had lost all impulse to join them. Her life
seemed to be ebbing away.

She felt no pain. She just lay there baking in the sun,
sleeping or half-sleeping, without desire to eat or move. Her
coat turned a faded brown colour and scaled almost completely away around her head and flippers, and in a stripe
down the middle of her back. It was a sort of half-
death.

Then one day her playmate climbed slowly on to the floe.
A week before she would have snaked forward to welcome
him. Now she lay as still as an ice-hummock, unaware that
her loneliness had ended.

The yearling came crawling along at an angle to her.
His fur too had lost its sleekness and colour around his head.
He also had been rejected by his fellows and driven off to
live—or die—alone until he grew like them again.

He came slithering along the ice, and fell over the Wanderer, rolling back in obvious alarm. The reason the stranger
played and hunted by sound, the reason why he had shown
so little aversion to this intruder from a different seal-nation,
was a simple one.

The strange yearling was blind.

Long ago in an undersea flurry evading a diving bear his
eyes had been clawed out and his face scarred. The scars
had healed, and he had learnt to find food and catch fish,
guiding himself by face-hair recordings of water movements

without the use of sight. Probably he found this possible because all seals hunt fish at times in muddy river-mouths where they cannot see what they pursue. Blind seals, strong and fat, and with their eye-sockets healed, have been photographed; their existence is one more proof of the adaptive miracle of wild life.

Wakened by his touch, the Wanderer stirred, then flung herself against him and mouthed him with the kissing motion that seals often make. He knew her then at once—his sense of smell would have warned him of her nearness, but for his fear at being expelled from the others. Moulting animals lose some of the keenness of their senses, too.

The Wanderer began to awaken from her moulting-trance from that day. Overjoyed to be no longer alone, as her playmate sank into sun-baked dreams she emerged from them. Soon other yearling seals climbed shamefacedly into the moulting-lair and sank down, shabby, soiled, and peeling. They seemed eager only to drop on to the snow and be forgotten now that their beautiful fur coats were ruined.

As they grew daily more despondent, she crept about the ice in growing pleasure. She was revelling in the clean new muscular sensations of her young body. More than the coat changes in wild things at this time. She felt remade. Before, she had scratched at the peeling skin-patches furtively. Now she looked smug, eagerly scraping away the brown harsh hair so as to disclose under it a brand-new ashy-grey coat, silky and glossy as a bird's wing. It had far fewer of the dark spots of youth, and she behaved as if she knew herself to be at last growing up, handsome, sleekly shapely, and well-dressed.

One day she went *splash* into the water again. It felt a thousand times more joyful after the weeks of penance, and she curved away like a dark streak. Often she crawled up on the ice beside her playmate. Once she took a fish and tried to share it with him, thrusting a piece towards him and playfully bunting him in the side. But till his vigil was over he would not eat, and she had no objection to finishing the fish herself.

Then one day he was swimming with her again in a glorious new fur coat to match her own. The sun seemed to invigorate the sparkling water with twice its usual power. They leapt and raced and bubbled up and down, rejuvenated, clothed, warmed, and made pretty by Nature's seasonal renewal.

The springtime nights were less prolonged now in that Polar latitude. By day the air seemed to shine. Under this summering sky, and especially at nights, a weird, pervasive excitement stirred the seal-herd, and each member emerging from the moulting-lair with peerless coat added to it. The annual process of wardrobe-renewal had fermented something else, which now peremptorily demanded release.

There came a dawn when it seemed as if the entire sea had filled overnight with dog-like heads. They broke the surface so close together that there could hardly have been space to tread water.

Excited and unafraid, the Wanderer pushed about with her playmate at her shoulder. She became anxious and expectant, spreading and receiving the same mounting emotion from all the rest of the new-clad herd.

The water was yeasty with them, the ice-floes crawled with them. There was a continual sort of ritual exchange between sea and ice, new-furred glistening seals clambering up or diving down in perpetual motion. They stirred the whole area of the sea like bubbles in a cauldron.

Then this movement, widespread as far as the eye could see, slowly fashioned itself into a sea-dance, wild and yet ordered as the march of waves under a rising wind. It took the shape of endless broad, dark waves of heads, with pale sea-troughs between. As the lines of swimming seals glided slowly forward certain old adults sprayed out before them. The black saddle-marks on their new fur coats shone in the sun while they displayed themselves in a rhythmic pattern of twist and return.

F

At first the wave-lines of heads seemed to be hardly moving. Then at the pulse of some invisible blood-heat the furry dancers suddenly quickened, rolling along, reproducing unconsciously with their bodies the rise and fall of storm-crested waves. Up they came all together, showing their shoulders while half-standing out of the water—down they went till only the broad swathes of black heads, so close as to be almost touching, swept swiftly along.

With the excitement at heart-breaking point, the ends of the horizon-flung lines began to curve backward. They slowly bent into miles-long crescents while the centres bulged forward.

In each line seals from behind leapt forward, half in the air, half-sliding over the slippery backs of the swimmers in front with a swift and lovely display of new coats. It looked as though dark waves were breaking. Up they came and over and down, in timed universal splashes.

The Wanderer, her soft brown eyes hazed with excitement, kept strict place with the rest. She rose and curved and showed her coat and fell instinctively. The blind yearling kept pace at her side. This was her initiation, but she would forget it. Yet every year she would dance and show a new fur coat afresh.

Each time that splash of thousands of falling swimmers smacked the water, the drumming in her blood reached a zenith that stirred every stretched nerve.

This was more than a seasonal display of Nature's new fur fashions. The seals were whipping themselves to the frenzy of excitement needed to face the perils of a migration journey of two thousand miles.

At last, when it seemed that the Wanderer could bear no more, that if this flashing, accelerating rhythm did not stop she must die, a single seal shot out ahead of the rest. He came from the centre of the first backward-bending line just at the point where it looked as if it must break. Tearing over the surface in a smother of bright foam, his new coat shone for a moment more vivid than them all.

A sigh like a sea-wind passed from horizon to horizon and covered the sea. Then the curving waves bent back into V-formation, and the whole assembly began to glide forward at a fast and easy speed.

Leading them was the one the Eskimos, who know most about the uncountable seal-people sweeping to and fro past their shores, say is chosen at this time every year. They call him the Seal King, an old traveller elected to guide his nation on its migration way.

Tens of thousands of seals fell into place behind him as he glided off through the seas. The springtime dance of the new fur coats was over.

10. Swim, Hunter, Swim!

MANY weeks passed, and now the seal-multitude was romping south in summer weather past the high-walled fjords and sky-supporting mountains of East Greenland. There the Wanderer, tingling with adolescent life-force, found the ice-burdened sea an equal playmate.

A teeming current was piling the floes south. The swimming sea-dogs seething in the wake of the Seal King curved after him like a flight of birds, so that now the foaming masses of ice were tumbling among them. This was fun, this was the breath of living, to dodge the overwhelming white walls, to see the Seal King ahead flash full-length out of the water and playfully copy him. Up he came, the sun smacking his gleaming back as he curved over and down. Then every seal played follow-my-leader, and leapt airborne and headed back into the sliding water-light. They came up grinning, breaking the waves as thousands obediently rose and splashed behind.

It was a journey without a time-table. At random the Seal King turned aside, slithered on to the edge of a mass of ice, and within ten minutes all the mariners had landed.

They lay so close together that from a little distance it looked as if the big white islands had turned solid grey. There they sprawled sunning themselves, scratching, stretching, rolling over on their backs, while the great floes glided slowly south and the smaller ice crashed and cannonaded past.

The Wanderer and the blind yearling, with a score more of that same careless age, had come leap-frogging along, lazy and late, in the rear of the swimming host. They grew excited at noticing that the older seals had left conspicuously vacant the sunniest and most attractive floe of all, one that was jammed in a mass of ice frozen between two promontories. It had settled in its place slightly tipped so that it caught the full weight of the summer sun.

With youth's deadly and beautiful rashness they raced each other to it. The Wanderer was there first, and slid snugly across the ice, leaving space for the rest. The blind yearling pressed after her, then the others, opening their mouths as though laughing at their elders who had after all missed the best resting-place.

They settled down to sleep in the sun close to each other, unsuspicious of all the world. On the bigger floes farther out seal-heads popped up in unending alerts, but the yearlings gave their perfect bodies unconditionally to the sun's petting and slept soundly, leaving all sentry-go to the care of elderly timidity.

They did not see the flat-faced little man in sealskin furs, standing distant and small, watching them. He had come to this spot as inevitably as they. As the fly-fisher knows where the trout will rise, as the fox crouches where the rabbit will run, so this Eskimo hunter knew from day to day the changing places where passing seals hauled themselves out to rest. He had been waiting here for two hours, and now he waited still, watching expressionlessly. Only once, when that group of flippered hobbledehoys had come rolling along and the whiskers of their elders stiffened as if in disapproval while they landed on the empty floe, had the hunter burst into noiseless laughter.

Hidden behind a hummock, he bent over the little, light sledge beside him, and erected in front of it a patch of white bear-fur on a frame. He thonged on to his feet squares of bear-skin with the fur downward to enable him to walk on the snow without sound. He tied a bear-skin pad to his left thigh reaching to the knee, and another round his left elbow. Finally he lay down on the snow behind the little sledge.

The white fur screen hid it and him, fading imperceptibly into the white background so that no sleepy glance would be able to identify it. Lying on his left side he crawled sound-lessly along on the bear-skin pads, pushing the sledge before him. The angle of his approach kept the sun full in front, for he had been taught as a little boy that if the sun was behind him or to one side the seals would grow suspicious of a shadow that jerked strangely. Instead, the shadows of the sledge and of himself were hidden now behind the white shield.

His movements were extremely slow. He knew that in such a stalk as this it might take him an hour to get near enough to strike down his victims. He inched along with the terrible patience of the creature that hunts to live. His only weapons were a knife and a harpoon, such as his ancestors had used for thousands of years. The harpoon on the sledge was a piece of perfect craftsmanship, made in un-hurried hours by the light of seal-blubber lamps in his hut. Its shaft was polished wood ending in a tapered seal-bone rod. This was tipped with a seal-bone barb, joined on so that when the barb embedded itself in the victim's body the rod fell away. To the barb was attached a slick sealskin thong about forty feet long, coiled as neatly as a spring.

The Arctic hunter shuffled himself forward while the young seals slept. His blubbery lips moved silently, perhaps in prayer, perhaps mouthing a prehistoric hunting-chant.

On he came, as noiseless as a patch of mist, knees drawn up, fur-soft foot set in the snow, body slowly straightening on

its furry slides—a hunting-beast rather than a man. A little
auk floated lazily down to look at him, then sailed abruptly
higher. Had they been watching, the yearlings on the floe
would have taken warning at that and slid off into the sea.
But no head was lifted to look.

The hunter moved forward, his lips delightedly shaping
his thoughts. Seal-meat steaming savourily in a cooking-pot
in his lone stone hut. The soft warmth of seal-entrail membranes cured into underclothing. The sinews his wife would
make into thread to sew them. The little seal-bones for
needles, the big ones he would steam and bend to frame a
new kyak of the sealskin. Other bones he would use for
sledge-runners, knives, harpoon-tips, so that not a scrap be
wasted. The creamy blubber with its faint nutty flavour, so
delicious to eat—but first must be fed those little lamps to
repel the Arctic darkness and the long night's cold. His eyes
narrowed, seeing new sealskins for boats, tents, clothes, beds
—even the littlest bits for thongs, or for his fat babies to
chew. He grinned—a killer's grin.

He had to kill. If he failed, or if the seal-herds were frightened by too many clumsy attacks and deserted these shores,
he, his wife, his children, his dogs, all his tribe must die.
Along the Arctic coasts there are human boneyards where
once stood villages. But the seals deserted them.

The Eskimos tried to live on walrus, narwhal, bears, foxes,
wolves. They put down hunks of meat with long bone-
needles hidden in them. Creatures bolted the bait, and died
when the needles pierced their bowels. But it was not
enough. The lamps began to gutter for lack of blubber-oil.
The freezing, starving humans glared at each other. Stabbing
arms rose and fell, and men began hacking off slices of flesh,
gnawing at children's bones. The survivors grew fewer, and
fought and ravened and died.

These things happen in our time. Such villages have been
visited—unpeopled, silent with something colder than the
silence of the most desolate snowfield; and from these

cannibal boneyards modern explorers move unhappily away.
For a moment they have glimpsed the world slid back a little
step proclaiming again that when the beasts go we human
animals must die.

The Eskimo could feel such things in his seal-nurtured
flesh and in the marrow of his bones.

Sixty yards away from the seals he stopped. The blind
yearling, hearing in his sleep a sound inaudible to those
whose senses are served by eyes, was lifting his head, listening, smelling at the air. But the hunter was down-wind.
With primitive sharpness he could smell the cold and fishy
odour of the seals, but they could not smell him. After a
long time the blind seal lay down. The hunter did not move,
but lay grinning madly in anticipation of the next step in the
old game. It came. Several minutes later, the blind seal,
which had been shamming sleep, sat up again. Nothing
moved. Relaxing, he sank down and slept.

The Eskimo knew the alarm had been given by the runners
of his sledge whispering on the snow. He took up his harpoon. It was mounted ready on a throwing-stick whose
ivory grip was beautifully carved with seal-hunt scenes. He
slid the coiled thong along his arm.

Leaving the sledge, he lay down and began to writhe towards the seals, as slowly as something in a nightmare. One
arm forward—one knee doubled—both tediously straightened; it was hard to see that his body moved, yet it almost
floated nearer.

The Wanderer's head came up. She looked round uneasily. Her eyes rested full on the unbreathing, furry lump
now thirty feet away. In water, because of the different
refraction, she could have seen at that distance a pulse of
ferocity thudding at the back of the man's cheek as his face
pressed deep into the snow. This strange thing had no
motion. Sealskin-clad, it looked much like any other seal.

The man's right hand gripped the throwing-stick of his
harpoon. His left clutched a handful of snow as if it had

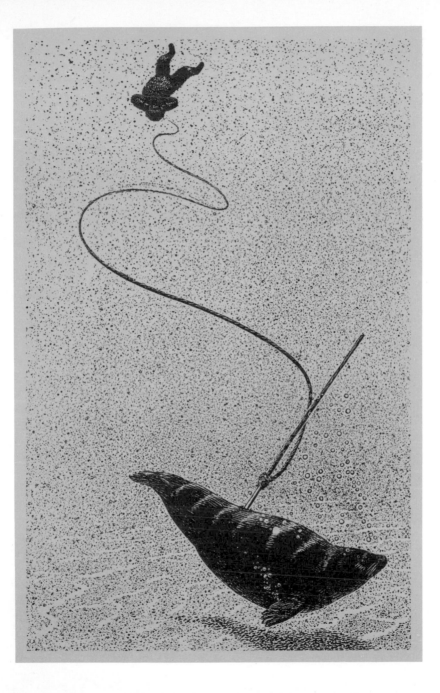

been frozen rigid. Under his gloves his knuckles were bursting white. He was biting his tongue to stop himself laughing, and the blood ran salt in his mouth. He dared not swallow lest the seals should hear the sound.

The Wanderer lay down. Some time later the man's body drifted forward. He was moving to pass between the seals and the water so that when he stood up they would turn away from him in terror inland. Seals who turn inland in such a case are doomed.

The Wanderer's head lifted again, and at the movement the blind yearling moved too. Both stared at the man's still body. In his mind a problem of life and death posed itself with Arctic clarity. He was just too far away to throw his harpoon or to run between the seals and the sea. Yet now others were stirring, their shoulders shifting as if to flee. His face was buried in the snow, but his mind saw what his eyes could not see.

His case was desperate, and he played his last trick. With arms forced to his sides and hands curving down like foreflippers, he bent his body in a backward curve and raised head and shoulders by muscles alone. His imitation of a listening seal was ridiculously perfect; and his sense of the ludicrous twisted his stomach as he rigidly held the long-learned hunter's pose. Staring at the seals, his flat and savage face pitifully strained, he opened his mouth and uttered the complaining bleat of a young seal.

The sound was exact, breathed out of a body of the right shape and size, clad in seal-fur. With vague curiosity the seals that had been just about to slither away stayed to stare. As they looked it cried out softly once again. There was no threat in the call; they had heard such a sound ten thousand times. The strange creature's head and shoulders sank with just the undulatory sway that any other seal would show when all cause for alarm had gone. Like human animals ashamed to be different from their neighbours, they all sank down with absurdly similar movements.

Two minutes later the furred figure drifted noiselessly on.

He was within throw. Two more yards and he could cut off the group, spring on them as they fled, knife them ...

Simultaneously they were all slithering away and he was on his feet, his harpoon singing through the air, a pierced seal grunting, the man bounding between the rest and the sea, his barbed harpoon-head sunk in one animal's neck, the thong loosely looped about his left wrist, his knife raised in his right hand.

The Wanderer, the blind yearling, and a dozen more squirmed away inland, the wounded one struggling after them. The rest, better placed, tipped into the sea and dived out of sight. Grinning, his lips red from his bitten tongue, the hunter yelled and waved his arms to shepherd the panicking victims away from the water as he overtook them, knife in hand.

He made a fatal error. Too excited, he raced on his bear-skin pads on to a lane of thin and new blue ice. It would hold him—his instinct on ice was like a seal's in water. But what he had never imagined was that the terrified seals would turn in their tracks and charge straight back at him! Never having learned, never having seen it done, they instinctively adopted tactics not uncommon among hunted seals. All together they flung themselves, half a ton of united and purposeful weight, precisely on to the weak joint where the thin blue ice was attached to the main mass.

The new ice disintegrated. Flinging up his hands, the hunter swivelled and leapt to save his life. He jumped short. Simultaneously the seals sank and vanished, and he sank too. With the rest went the harpooned seal, slowly swimming down towards the depths after its companions. Broken shags of floating ice tipped about the disturbed water.

The Eskimo came to the surface. His gloved fingers clutched at the ice-edge, a piece broke away in his hands, and he sank, holding it. He came up again, flung an arm wide over the edge, tried to sling a leg up—and then the thong looped over his wrist and still attached to the wounded seal suddenly tightened, dragging at him. Again the ice broke under him, and he went down, very slowly towed by the seal.

He struggled wildly under the water, trying to free his wrist. His heavy clothes were sodden and icy. For a moment he was swimming, dragging the wounded seal, then it was dragging him. Big fat bubbles streamed up over his head to the distant surface, and gathered unbroken at the edge of the floe.

The Wanderer, no longer alarmed, came swimming round in a circle, and from a distance mildly observed him. His arms and legs were sailing loosely like those of a sinking doll. As a twist of the thong fouled one arm and bound it to his side she went away like a streak. The line floated over his neck and was pulled tight as the dying seal made a last flurry to escape. More bubbles streamed away from him, and the thong curved over one of his feet.

Fantastically, and slowly waving one arm and one leg, the others bound to his body, he rolled down after the seal he had caught.

11. *Big Fight*

THE young seals swam on and on, down the coast, trailing behind the rest of the herd. Those prudent adults had slithered off their floes when the little auk flew startled up over the Eskimo hunter. The death of one yearling caused no more concern than the fall of one leaf off a tree.

A fjord looked inviting, and the swimming multitude poured into it, their heads gleaming among the golden wavelets. This fjord was very deep, but near its mouth was a threshold of fairly shallow water. The seals found, occupying the vicinity of one part of this undersea hilltop, a small colony of walruses, each ten feet long, enormous in girth, stiff-whiskered, and peaceful. Some were digging out bivalves from the ooze with their tusks. Others sunned themselves on ice-floes and meditatively watched the seal thousands separate into two streams to pass them by. One of the walruses opened his mouth and roared in a playful sort of way.

Farther up, the fjord narrowed between cliffs screaming and chattering with thousands of birds. A score of ledges were thronged, and the air was filled with the birds like a snowstorm. Kittiwakes, gulls, guillemots, eider ducks, and

innumerable others clamoured, quarrelled, fought, glided
on to the water, or swept whirring into the air. Some trick
of sunshine, caught in an unusual angle of the sheltering cliffs
and warming the sea estuary and the cold fjord's deep waters,
caused regular seasonal drifts up from the bottom of mollusc
food, and attracted seals, walruses, and birds alike. Between
them they turned this cleft in a barren coast into a roaring
metropolis of creature life, booming and barking, whistling
and squawking and shrieking in a babel of animal tongues.

They had done more. A rain of fish-fed manure washed
down from the bird rookeries had created in a few clefts and
hollows a rich soil. Already this was flushing with the fever-
ish vegetation of the Arctic. Scentless flowerbuds, opening
with the almost explosive force needed for reproduction
during that brief summer, had been unable to wait until
the snow had gone. Patches of tall buttercups, dainty hare-
bells, red and yellow saxifrages, heavenly blue gentians, and
white and yellow poppies made futurist designs and blobs
in the Arctic desolation.

The low Polar sun warmed these sloping pockets of de-
cayed manure, raising temperatures there almost magically
above those of the surrounding air. The head of the fjord
was blocked by a stupendous glacier. Water, melting from
its heights in early summer, had spread layers of glacial
debris at its sides and had saturated the lower ground with
ice-water bogs and morasses, tufted here and there with
white cotton-grass.

The fjord birds constantly hunted the estuary under the
cliffs of the protecting promontory. Often they would sweep
in fishing-flocks far out to sea, staring down with unwavering
eyes into the tossing water. The little snow-buntings would
hop about the ice-floes shrilling, among the hosts of the
screechers and squawkers, their sweet and solitary song.

All through the short nights, as the world spun round with
the sun barely below its northern rim, the Arctic sky reflected
splendid changing hues—golden, scarlet, and imperial purple.

The indigo clouds were edged royally with gold, higher up the colours changed through green to blue, and finally to the dark vault of heaven.

One day, when the Wanderer and the blind yearling were companionably food-hunting far down the fjord, they ventured right out to the walrus-bank in the estuary. The Wanderer wanted to see what the birds were eating, and did not know that curiosity can kill.

As the two idled along a seal of another breed, almost twice as big as themselves, came swimming up under the steep rock wall, and seeing them ahead, turned towards the sea again. The Wanderer followed this dark-backed giant, and the blind yearling sculled after her. The big seal looked back at them now and again, and increased his speed. He skirted the edge of the fjord in deep water, leading them into a cliff-edged tiny bay whose narrow entrance opened opposite the undersea walrus-bank. Then as they trailed him round its shore and drew too near for his liking he turned menacingly, the skin suddenly inflating high over his nose, like a snake about to strike. The two pursuers flashed round and away towards the cliffs, and the hooded seal dived without out a ripple, and swam away under water out to sea.

This was a new and exciting place to explore. The Wanderer and her companion examined the dark crannies of water-washed rock, and dived eagerly into holes at one end and out at another. They frisked and chased about while the walruses, with portly gravity and looks of whiskered surprise, sank through the clear water to excavate their mollusc-bank or rose to sun themselves on the glittering floes and blink momentously.

It was a scene of primeval peace. But in nature peace never lasts. A ten-foot drift of white fur passed noiselessly across the promontory and sank in the sea out of sight of the two playing seals. With only a black nose-tip showing, it began to swim towards an ice-floe, floating above the undersea walrus-bank. The moment had been patiently chosen.

All the walruses were under water, except one mother affectionately holding her baby in a fore-flipper to her breast. She was cruising idly, sitting upright in the water, and the bear kept the floe between himself and her.

Presently she pushed her baby on to the floe, partly with her head and partly with her shoulder. It scrambled a little way from the edge, and the mother, after contentedly eyeing it, and taking a look round for danger, submerged.

Before the small thing could cry out or even feel any fear the bear had swept up on to the ice and killed it with a single massive bite across the neck. Killer and victim were still. Then the bear's head swayed as he looked nervously and swiftly around. He was thin-shanked, starving, and desperate, or he would never have risked this. Licking the blood on his lips, he looked greedily down. But he dared not start the meal for which his stomach was grumbling. He lifted the walrus-baby in his jaws and slipped into the water to swim round the high point to land.

At that moment the mother walrus's head broke the water a few feet from him. Her half-human face, with its absurd two-foot tusks like drooping whiskers, contorted into a grimace and she uttered a half-choked cry. It was not very loud, but there was a savagery in it that was frightful to hear. The bear snarled soundlessly at her, rolling his lips over the teeth that held her dead baby, and swam steadily away.

But that strangulated, hoarse sob must have been heard by the animals rooting far down beneath the water. Huge heads popped up all round. The faces that had been so ridiculous became suddenly terrible as, with a seething and churning of waters, they closed on the bear. An old bull, weighing over a ton, cut like a tug across the swimmer's path, and, raising himself half out of the water, stabbed down with sabre-like tusks. The bear dived, still obstinately holding the baby. He dodged that murderous blow only to find another walrus striking at him underwater from one side.

A scarlet mouth burst open on his shoulder where a touch from the ivory cut through the matting of his fur, and the water reddened. His little eyes wild with rage, he surfaced once more.

As his head reappeared, savagely peering round, he realized he was trapped. The walruses had him in an unbroken circle, and as if to show how sure they were of killing him one put its head down and butted him in the flank. The bear uttered a great grunt of agony, for a walrus can poke its head up through ice four inches thick.

Opening his jaws, he let the dead cub float away, and in the same movement sprang over the surface of the water at the old bull who had first stopped his escape. There was an immense flurry, a fearful crunch, a scream, and the bull went reeling away with feeble spasmodic jerks of his fore-flippers. The bear grinned like a death's-head, but before he could turn a tusk-blow from the mother of the dead baby gouged out half the side of his neck. His mighty head fell forward, its teeth spasmodically clicking, as another walrus came up from beneath and ripped open his belly.

Those who attack these inoffensive and affectionate monsters do so at their peril; the white bear would hunger no more. He sank under the water. Some bubbles streamed up, and slowly the turbulence subsided. A little way away the old walrus bull lay coughing painfully. The bereaved mother caught up her dead baby, looked at it with bewilderment, and let it float away.

The Wanderer and the blind yearling, terrified as mice, skulked deep underwater, flitting in panic first this way, then that. The conflict of the titans took place near the exit from their bay. They were trapped with their backs to the high cliffs, and ahead of them a welter of foam and unimaginable fear.

The noises died away in spasms of grunting and roaring. After a long time the blind yearling moved nervously towards the exit from the bay. Bear and walruses had gone. The place seemed always to have been empty of life. The two seals slipped through furtively, and turned, at the top of their silent speed, up the fjord. There was no pursuit. In a minute their fears evaporated. They played in and out of the crannies of the rock walls on their way back towards their own people.

The seal-herd spent some time in the fjord, and no enemies approached them. The Arctic summer was mellow in that secret place. The sun shone continuously, hot enough presently to bring humming mosquitoes from the bogs beside the glacier-head. Big, solitary bees went bumbling about among the flowers, and once a brown fritillary butterfly floated down on a rock and opened and shut its wings in pretty vanity. Floating ice occasionally came nosing up the fjord from the outer sea, where the steady current down the Greenland shore bore all the rubbish of the Polar seas steadily along.

Sometimes the rain came sheeting, stimulating the seals to play extravagant games. They took long leaps out of the water, as if trying to swim in the rain, sat upright on the surface, and opened their mouths.

They were much thinner at this time of year, and generally lazier than they had been. They went out in big parties to the mouth of the fjord and sunned themselves on ice-floes, partly to bask in summer's leisure, partly to digest the food gathered during their hunting-hours. Most of their more active time was spent below the surface, diving and fishing for five- or ten-minute spells.

Over their heads, when their play took them far up the fjord, the seals saw the wall of ice where the glacier rose catching the rays of the summer sun. The incessant washing of the warmer water had eaten away the ice on the fjord surface, so that it curved out in a stupendous overhang.

Beneath this it was the habit of all the seals to play water-games, racing along in single file, sweeping up in line-abreast to meet another line, diving, leaping, and sprawling. At

G

certain times of day the sun deflected green from part of the
ice-wall, flooding the water in a translucent light which
seemed to drive the swimmers to a frenzy.

There came a day of rain falling through intensely clear
sunshine. The radiance of a rainbow spread, catching the
angle of the ice and bathing the pool below in colours of red
and yellow, orange and violet, projected on the flowing surface of marbled green.

With a continual splashing the seals leapt through the
colours as the rain slowly ceased. As the transformation
faded, their energy died, and presently everything in the
pool was silent, hundreds of heads flecking with spots of
brown the pale meadows of the sea.

Suddenly breaking over their heads came a dreadful noise,
while a tremor ran down the curving wall of ice that swung
so far out over them. More a feeling than a movement, this
passed like a great shudder into the sea.

12. *Birth of an Iceberg*

After a moment's silence the warning noise was followed by a sudden report as of a cannon.

An immense piece of the front of the glacier above their heads, twice the height of a church steeple, began to slide, and smashed into the sea among the fleeing seals. Its impact sounded like the breaking of a board a hundred feet wide. As it plunged down out of sight a score of cataracts poured after it. From the boiling depths where the iceberg had disappeared there arose a mighty grinding sound while clouds of spray shot into the air and fell like a cloudburst.

Several seals, struck by the calving iceberg, had been instantly killed. The rest, the Wanderer among them, were tossed about the pool. Some were hurled high against the rock walls, and fell back dying. The Wanderer was washed outward towards the mouth of the fjord, rolled over, and smothered in falling water, but she escaped injury.

After a short time the iceberg reappeared. Out of the inferno of the agitated sea it raised its head fully sixty feet above the surface, water pouring down from all parts of it. It laboured there, leaning one way and then another, as if

doubtful on which side it should fall. Near-by seals dashed
away below water to escape the monster's renewed attack.

With another dreadful grinding as some of its internal
caves collapsed, the ice-mountain rolled heavily on to its
side. It rocked violently about for some minutes and finally
settled, floating in the middle of the wave-churned pool.
Dead or dying seals washed helplessly against its sides.
Another seal went slowly down as the berg swayed.

The summer sun and pressure from behind had cracked off
this great berg weighing perhaps a hundred thousand tons.
Streams of water were still cascading down its sides. And
there was a continual cracking noise from the escape of
confined air and the breakage of ice in caverns and on
projecting surfaces where splits had been made by the giant
fall.

The seals reeled away from it, avoiding the spurs of ice
which stabbed in all directions from its base, menacing them
hundreds of feet down in the water as it swayed. The sunny
sea turned cold, and an icy breathing moved between the
rock walls. The top of the berg glittered, catching the sunlight like a lighthouse window. A dark forefoot of ice struck
the fjord side with the force of a ramming battleship and
broke off with a splitting crack. The berg gobbled and
thundered as it reeled back from the blow. The sea boomed
in its caverns.

Already the seals were streaming away from the pool that
had been for so long their playground. As they went they
fell into the compact and determined movement of migration. They glided rapidly down the fjord and poured out into
the open sea. The bodies left at the bottom of that fissure in
the iron coast were already forgotten, and the injured, limp-
ing farther and farther behind, were abandoned to sink or
swim as best they might.

In a few minutes the shocks of the iceberg's birth and every
conscious memory of the fjord itself had slipped away from
the seals' understanding. They played and slid over each

other, diving, standing up on their tails and then racing
to overtake, with perfect physical delight.

They swept along south-westward, lifted by the current
that carried innumerable ice-floes along as companions.
Sometimes a single ivory gull would float overhead across
the pale blue, or hover motionless in the distance and utter
a long, melancholy, fluting cry.

Once as the seals rolled along there was a sudden spouting
of the sea two miles ahead. It was caused by a whale leaping
full-length out of the sea to rid himself of parasites clinging to
his body. Such a splash can be seen ten miles away from a
ship's masthead.

They saw the whale not long afterwards, drowsing sickly
on the surface. There was something obviously wrong with
this old leviathan. He hung there, flaccid and fallen, and
the greyish head that stared at them had such a hurt,
ferocious expression in the red little eyes under their frowning
ridges that the seals swung far out to avoid him.

As they did so a gull, sliding low over the waves, touched
down on the whale's arched back. At the touch he vanished
in terror with a smash of horizontal tail-flukes. The seals
saw him sink till he faded out of sight.

The gull slid unalarmed up into the air and hung there
while the disturbance subsided, stooping once to pick from
the uprush of the water a fish, which was swallowed at a
gulp. The seals went pouring past, using these new waves to
play in, equally unconcerned about whale, gull, or fish.

Later, as the seals amused themselves about an ice-floe,
something came tearing over the sea leaving a heaving wake
of white foam. It was the old whale, his outward-arched
mouth open like a cave into which the sea and all its plankton
flowed. When he closed his jaws the water rushed out again,
but the plankton was sieved by the eight-foot-long whalebone
strainers in the monster's mouth, and presently swallowed,
joining two tons or so of food already lying in that enormous
stomach.

As dramatically as he had come the whale stopped, and lay again on the water as if poisoned. He lay abandoned amid acres of the slippery sea-food he could no longer eat. The plankton washed blindly up and down his mountainous sides, infinitesimal, but living against the dying mass.

Again the whale burst into sudden desperate activity. He sounded, plunging far down and away ahead of the seals, moving heavily, as if crippled by a mortal wound.

Many miles farther on along the coast the Wanderer was swimming fifty feet below the surface, hunting for something to eat.

A flicker zipped away to one side, and she flashed after it. It doubled to and fro, but she turned with it. It seemed to spring upward, then flip down, but still she pursued. There was a cruel beauty in this ballet of the two shadows in the green depths. They moved in curves like silent music, and it seemed as though they did not hurry, but kept their distance from each other. Then with a lovely sway the Wanderer leaned sideways, taking the fish in her jaws. It tremored convulsively there, and she turned lazily over, holding it in her fore-flippers, like tiny hands, as she ate its life away.

Not until then, with the blind concentration of the chase forgotten, did she realize that there was a monstrous shadow ahead. Had she been wiser she would have swerved in her tracks and fled away from it. Unknown shadows fifty feet below the sea's surface sometimes have teeth that crack bones, horny beaks, or thirty-foot tentacles that whip round the bodies of trespassers like wire ropes. But the Wanderer could only live, and must one day die, according to the powers and defects of her being. She allowed herself to float forward in an agony of nervous expectancy, fan-like hind-flippers tensed for the kick that would send her flashing away if anything threatened.

The body of the dead whale lay there, sagging over some undersea hilltop a little way out from the mountainous coast, very faintly moving with a motion shockingly like life. It had evidently been there for some time, and was partly eaten. A cloud of crabs, fishes, and other creatures thickened the water about it. Some of them leapt in and out on the morbid, fleshy mass, tearing away tiny mouthfuls. Some were attached firmly to it by suckers or claws or half-transparent trailers, camping, as it were, on the slopes of the dead. Eyes, lips, and tongue were gone, and the skin was pitted and nibbled. As the destroyers ravened and ate there were murderous dashes among them by killers attracted by the gathering of their carrion-eating prey.

The Wanderer floated up towards the whale's mountainous back, keeping out of range of the throng that rushed to and fro over the plains and expanses of the dead. She was excited and startled by the sight, unwilling to leave it, yet afraid to go too near. As she moved slowly up the hillside of the whale's shoulder three fifteen-foot shadows appeared ahead, gouging and excavating in a dirty fog of floating scraps.

They were sharks, gorged already until they could scarcely swim. But they turned and drifted a yard or two towards the Wanderer, forced by their killing instinct, though in their state they had no chance even of keeping her in sight for half a minute. She shimmered away, driven by a resurrected terror of that shark whose shoulder had scraped her more than a year ago when she was a cub near the White Sea.

This time there was no pursuit. The three brutes rolled heavily and exhaustedly back again, and once more buried their monstrous mouths in the dead whale's side, while round about them the cloud of scavengers thickened and flashed and swayed.

13. *Seal-boat Slayer*

ONE summer day the herd found a large sheltered bay with flat and comfortable ice-floes for sun-basking. Most of the seals slithered out of the water to rest and scratch and blink. But the yearlings could not resign themselves to this. They sported about in the water, attracting far too much attention by their noise. Their elders stirred uneasily, and seemed to frown on them with blinking eye and drooping whisker, as an old dog will frown at a frisking puppy.

This mattered not at all to the Wanderer and her friends. First they went looking for rose-fish, of which there were none for fifty miles. Inspired to wilder gaiety because the fastest dashes and steepest dives disclosed no fish, they began to swim races, scudding over the surface in utmost disrespect beneath the very noses of their irritably drowsing elders. Later the youngsters separated into little companionable groups and went exploring in all unsuitable directions.

As usual the Wanderer and the blind yearling were together. As usual, too, they were more rash than most. The blind one could not see his friend, but seemed to feel comfort in the Wanderer's presence. Each time her eyes looked his way he turned too, with comradeship in his scarred and sightless face.

The two of them romped round a headland and found with eager delight yet another new thing in the sea. A family party of huge creatures was playing in the water. There were a dozen adults, three times as big as the seals, and a miscellaneous assortment of youngsters, some fat and short, some lean and gangling. These strangers were narwhals; the bigger ones grey-white with leopard spots, the old males each with a single tooth monstrously projected into a spiral ivory tusk eight or nine feet long.

The two young seals trod water a good way off, the Wanderer watching with fascination three of these old unicorns of the sea engaged in a triangular fencing match. They dashed round each other in the water, elevating their horns and pausing as if in salute. Then they crossed them with a clash, stabbing mightily in thrust, parry, and riposte, yet with innocent playfulness. One touch from those hugely weighted tusks would have gouged out an eye, or ripped open a leathery side. Again and again it looked inevitable, yet within an inch the massive blow was turned.

Other males looked critically on. Meanwhile their mates and families lazily watched or sank below the surface on mysterious missions, suddenly popping up short and rounded heads with an air of surprise that their protectors should continue so long a sport so incongruous to their bulk.

Both the Wanderer and the narwhals saw stealing round the far distant point of the bay first one and then a little crowd of slim sea-creatures of a new sort. These newcomers had seal-hides waterproofed with seal-oil varnish. Their bones were the bones of seals, and they glided over the water swift and thin. Three times as long as a seal, but with scarcely any width at all, they slid along without ripple or splash.

They were Eskimo hunting-kyaks.

The whole depth of these racing-skiffs was little more than the palm of a man's hand. They were narrow as knives, and, except for a central manhole, were decked over their whole length with waterproof sealskin. Each bore in its bows a tiny shield of white behind which a man was hidden, his single paddle dipping silently, first one side, then the other. These men, with their undeveloped dwarf-like legs, designed as if by Nature to fit these depthless boats, were balancing continuously as one balances to ride a bicycle.

The decks of the kyaks were flush with the water. Each man had built his manhole to fit the shape of his own legs. A waterproof cap and apron was drawn so tight round forehead, cheeks, and chin as to cut into the blubbery flesh to make a watertight joint, and laced equally tightly to the edge of the manhole. In the excitements of hunting, in a rough sea, or perhaps at the blow of a vengeful bladder-nosed seal, the flimsy kyak rolls clean over with the hunter upside down under water. But not one drop can enter boat or clothing. All that gets wet is the front of the hunter's face as he rights himself and his cockle-shell with a single blow of his paddle.

In this part of Greenland, where only constant hunting can sustain life, a quarter of the Eskimos die in search of food. Because their lives depended on it, these men in their softly gliding kyaks were as tense as stalking beasts.

The narwhals saw them, and in two seconds the surface of the water in which they had been playing was bare, heaving heavily where monster bodies had slid below. Just as quickly, the two seals at their distant watch-point also submerged.

The advancing swimmers roused the Wanderer's curiosity, and the blind yearling instinctively relied for warning on the sounds she made. Only a foot or two underneath they felt safe. After three or four minutes the Wanderer's head reappeared on the surface, and she stole a swift look round.

The scene had changed. During that time, when no creature watched, the Eskimos had driven their leaf-light boats with long, powerful strokes. They slid the paddles along in their hands to get greater power, almost forcing the backs of their kyaks underwater and lifting the bows off. But now they were motionless, strung out across the area where the narwhals had been playing. Waiting.

From her distant point, and, as she thought, unobserved, because no man's head moved, the Wanderer watched the newcomers and found them dull. Yet there was something faintly menacing about the silent way they had come. She stayed where she was, treading water without a ripple. Then the blind yearling's head came up beside her.

There were some ice-floes about, rising and falling in the long, heavy swell under the pale blue sky from which the sun shone hot. An Arctic tern flew quietly past. After it had gone a long-tailed skua followed it across the shining infinity, and on out of sight. Not a man or a boat stirred from station. They rode up and glided down like driftwood on the long swells passing beneath them.

Suddenly there was an eruption in the water as an immense back broke the surface, arched over, and vanished. Narwhals are mammals; they must come up often for air to breathe.

"Krayduwere!"

The nearest hunter's whisper breathed across the sea. With two deep-dipping strokes he slid his seal-boat over to the spot and stopped it, hanging there poised. His harpoon in its throwing-stick, with carefully coiled forty-foot thong, lay in a tray on his boat's deck against his gloved hand.

Everywhere this man journeyed by water he would throw his harpoon or his light bird-lance at two- or three-minute intervals at any floating objects. Those up here who are not marksmen die.

Again the hunters were as quiet as if painted on a back-cloth of ice and sea. Their paddles lay flat on the water, balancing with imperceptible hand-movements their precarious skin-boats.

Some time passed. The two seals half slept in the water, half-watched the distant scene, making instinctive lazy movements to keep themselves afloat.

Two other great backs suddenly appeared. Both were too far away for a harpoon-throw, and instantly sank again. Hunters flashed to the spot, then lay there as if transfixed.

A smaller back emerged just in front of a kyak. A man's arm shot out; his harpoon sank in the vanishing back. The shaft floated away, leaving its head deep. The Eskimo swiftly hurled overboard an inflated sealskin float to which the barbed head was attached by its thong, then he swept his boat away as if possessed. In a vast swirl of water the line tightened, the float was dragged under the sea and disappeared.

Yelling, screeching, violently released after an hour's frozen silence, the hunters skimmed their seal-boats like gnats to the place where the strike had been made. They waited, silent, with harpoons upraised. After five minutes the float bobbed up. The boats swarmed there. A minute more and the narwhal emerged beside the float, was instantly pierced by other harpoons and vanished, this time dragging several inflated floats below. To hold these air-filled skins under water was too great a strain for the wounded beast. Almost at once he came up.

Men's arms lanced more harpoons into him. He thrashed round the crimson surface, scattering his tormentors. Then he grew feeble and lay still. Screeching and singing, the men in the kyaks crowded round the nine-foot body, with its great flat tail and fallen ivory horn.

Two kyaks of the men who first harpooned it closed in. Paddles were laid across to steady them, and one man bent over and cut a hole in the dead narwhal's back, gouging between blubber layer and skin. Leaning cautiously down and putting his mouth to the hole, he blew the skin up like a balloon, growing redder and redder in the face at his difficult task, while all his friends laughed and cheered. Finally another man passed him a lace, and he fastened the orifice shut. Had he not done this the infinitely precious carcase would have sunk in a few minutes. Now, inflated with air and with the floats removed, it would be towed several miles through the ice-floes home—so long as no storm arose. And if the elements raged these flat-faced hunters would fight them as cunningly as they had fought the narwhal. Each man was willing to risk death so that the monster should be dragged to shore, to give meat, blubber, skin, oil, bones, sinews—the precious stuffs of life itself.

The fleet of kyaks turned bobbing and leaping to escort the dead narwhal home. The paddlers wildly waved their harpoons. Some yelled with laughter, others chanted snatches of traditional hunting-songs. The very boats seemed to dance an accompaniment.

An hour's silence had been a penance to these voluble and merry people, whom ethnologists say are the happiest and healthiest race of all mankind, laughing more in a month than their civilized brothers do in a year. Though the Eskimos hunt as pitilessly as beasts, the hunt and all life is a game to them. The most reluctant of peoples to leave their homeland, and then frantic to get back, they laugh uproariously at white traders, so careful and troubled about so many things, who call themselves civilized.

They are free of all our fears of war and poverty. Being virtually innocent of laws, they have only two punishments —public disapproval and death. Neither is inflicted until public opinion is universal, perhaps after years of discussion. Only made articles are private. All the rest is common, so there is simply no competition for wealth or goods.

These men of the village fishing-fleet would have thought any quarrel about their hunt profits the act of maniacs. The first harpooner, because his skill had benefited them all, could claim the horn and one hunter's prime portion of meat and bone. All the rest would be jointed, share and share alike. Joints would then be cut up among friends at home. When the meat was in the cooking-pots the housewives would shout from their doors for all within hearing to come and eat.

Sinews, bones, blubber, oil, and the rest would be shared. The skin would be awarded by public acclaim to the villager who needed it most. The work of cutting up, the manufacture of communal items, the cooking, and the cleaning—all would share. The proudest man in the community, whose influence was greatest, though no one had any authority over another, would be that one whose hut had most voluntary adherents—the Eskimo word is 'friends.' And these would normally include some blind or helpless people, whom he would support. To be head of such a group demonstrated to all the good hunter, the man of wisdom and resource—in their own words, "he who could help most." These people find it as natural as breathing to share the work and guidance of "him who can help most."

The harpooner who had first struck the narwhal was such a man. There was a great broad smile, now shining like the sun, across his face as he gracefully guided the leading kyak among the others with their towlines fastened to the inflated carcase. This man was a poet as well as a hunter. Like many Eskimos he could express his thoughts in a vocabulary in excess of ten thousand words, a range far greater than that of most civilized men. Eskimo is a language for poets— each word in its immense vocabulary has hundreds of different inflections, and each inflection gives a precise meaning, different from any other.

This hunter could not write, having no materials, and only sounds for words. He clothed the poems of his thoughts by singing them to traditional airs learned by ear. He pictured himself sitting in his hut with a stone tool, carving poem pictures on this great spiral horn. His lips shaped the pictures he would make. Hungry, weary, he smiled like a happy child. Life is more than food, the body is more than raiment, and this man knew it.

As the kyak fleet took formation one of the seal-boat hunters, with a swift, single stroke of his paddle, sent his craft zigzagging among the rest to glide up beside a friend.

He grunted a few words, his sloe-black eyes turning with merriment to the distant spot where the two seal-heads were still visible. Only health-clear eyes, trained to distances, could have seen two heads in the sea so far away.

He had been watching them patiently all the afternoon. His neighbour breathed a word. It ran whispering over the swell from boat to boat. Half a dozen kyaks detached themselves from the fleet and spun as if on pivots. Each man crouched behind his white camouflage-square, and began with noiseless movements to send his racing-skiff sliding through the sea. They edged out into a longish line, the hunter who had sighted the quarry taking the middle place. As unmenacing as driftwood, they began to float towards their new prey.

The Wanderer saw them coming. At first she was only drowsily interested. The blind yearling heard them even while the stealthy lip of their paddles was inaudible to his companion. But as she showed no alarm neither did he.

The white squares so slowly floating over the sea from different directions looked to the Wanderer much like the lumps of ice which swayed up and down between them. Sometimes the swell of the sea obscured one or more kyaks. In those moments they were driven forward with strokes that almost raised the slender things into the air. But when the swell subsided a dip of the paddle had already held them motionless again. Seals can neither count nor judge surface distances accurately. Though she felt irritably troubled, the Wanderer did no more than look quickly about.

The nearest hunter was barely forty yards away. His hand already gripped the throwing-stick of his harpoon when the blind yearling heard the man breathing and vanished soundlessly under the water. Without a ripple the Wanderer also disappeared. In the kyaks no word was spoken. The chief hunter pointed in several directions, and a boat slid to each. To the Eskimo a boat is not inanimate. Every kyak, every stone, every lump of ice has a soul that can be commanded by the proper magic word. They spend their lives discovering these words and practising sounds and gestures of command.

For five minutes no one moved. Perhaps the chief hunter was trying to communicate with the spirit of the sea that was hiding his victims from him. Perhaps he felt an answer to his thoughts. His hand motioned imperiously again. Two boats glided to fresh stations.

The Wanderer and her friend had not submerged deeply. Down there in the greenness they had been warned by no sound or tremor of the water. Now they surfaced together. Out of the corner of her eye the Wanderer saw a man's hand move, and she dived. But the blind yearling, unguided by sight, simultaneously heard her go and felt a thud of agony in his back.

He sank like a stone, half paralysed by a numbness spreading down one side, slowing his movements as if the sea had thickened about his limbs. To escape from it he rolled convulsively on one side and swam, much slower than his usual streak of escape, parallel with the surface.

So instantaneous had been the seal-boat hunter's harpoon-throw, and so difficult its angle, that the thong attached to the barbed head had fouled the kyak's white screen. Now, as the speared victim dashed under the boat, the line suddenly tightened, defeating the Eskimo's effort to unloose it and get the float overboard. The jerk tipped the narrow kyak upside down and tore his paddle out of his hands.

Held in his manhole and waterproofed by the skin-apron stretched from his head to the boat's deck, the hunter hung head down under the icy water. His contorted face was only a foot or two from the dying seal's back as it glided away from him.

14. Out of the Depths

HAD the Eskimo managed to keep his paddle, a single skilled stroke would have rolled his boat upright again. But the paddle had floated away. He struck at the water with the short throwing-stick of his harpoon, which remained in his hand. The kyak got half-way up, then slid back. After a second's pause he tried again, swung, hesitated agonizedly, then once more slipped upside down.

But this man was one of the few who in such a case had one trick left. Dropping the stick, he scrabbled with his hands, like a dog at a rabbit-hole. With amazing skill he scooped at the water, and slowly achieved a feat hardly any-one can perform. The kyak rolled two-thirds upright, paused; he seemed to snatch at the empty air, and righted himself. With a great gasp his imprisoned breath burst out of him. He leaned forward, panting as two other hunters, who had meant to pull him up if he had been unable to right himself, shot by.

The float had been pulled away and below by the blind yearling's frantic struggles to escape. Now float and seal drifted to the surface. His backbone had been injured by

H

the harpoon-stab. The paralysis stiffening his muscles had drugged his mind, and he lay collapsed on the water, drowsy and unafraid.

He could not see that there were men around him, and his unnaturally sharp hearing was already sinking to the last silence. He was conscious of the ever-friendly sea rippling with a long and soothing touch against his side. Another sound, almost as unmeaning as the song of the wind, faintly filtered through to him. It was the Eskimo, pausing with raised harpoon to intone a cheerful and friendly appeal to the seal's spirit not to be angry at what he was going to do. Had things gone the other way, and the jerk that overset the kyak drowned him, the hunter would have blamed the seal no more than the salt sea-water that choked him.

Perhaps this primitive dirge touched some chord in the dying creature's nerves. There was an approving murmur from the other hunters as the seal turned and exposed an unprotected belly, with the air of a tired child seeking through a more comfortable position a path direct to sleep. The spearman's poised arm stabbed down. Then the dead body rested on the sea's familiar breast, where it had been born and reared and fed.

The Eskimos smiled at each other gladly and quietly. The last-minute compliance to meet the spear-thrust had been a good omen. They began to sing in low voices as they manoeuvred the silky body on to the back of the seal-boat killer's kyak.

One of their own brotherhood of creatures had died that they might live, and they were more conscious of this sacrifice than many Christians are of the sacrifice of the Cross. Paddling quietly, balancing their kyaks, and singing as they went, they turned to black silhouettes against the Arctic sky, and so disappeared.

The Wanderer dived, twisting away under the seal-boat fleet till the light grew dim in the green water. Several times she looked round for the blind yearling, and then with a graceful and careless movement went gliding on again. Not surfacing until she was at the limit of her endurance, she came up to find the world empty.

Everything was peaceful. The floes swung up and down as the seas rolled under them, wavelets slapped their sides, the wind whispered past. The blind yearling was not there, and the Wanderer wanted to play. She dived again, exploring the underwater world for him. She remembered the narwhals, and looked for them, but they had gone. Finally, with the vague discomfort of the gregarious animal left too long alone, she began to quest back towards the distant bay where the seal-herd had been resting.

They were still there, blackening the ice. Even the yearlings were sleeping now. First on one floe, then on others, heads would be lifted, staring blindly round for dangers. Though the Wanderer slid through the seas as soundless as a fish, yet some warning ran ahead of her. A near-by seal gazed right at her in alarm, its eyes suddenly focusing from sleep. Then it sank down again. She climbed up beside it —there was always room for just one more on these crowded floes. Two or three times she looked round for her lost playmate. Then the drowsiness of a sleeping multitude dulled her doubts, and she also put her cheek against the snow and slept.

An hour later the seal-host moved, as if drilled to some silent command. One moment they lay in rows and splotches, like the victims of a mass slaughter. The next, the waves were boiling with them, and every piece of ice was swept clean. There had been no alarm, nor had any group's movements disturbed the others. Thousands took the water with a single plop. The Seal King went out ahead, the rest followed, a widespread pack of swimming dogs' heads, with innumerable eyes.

They swam on unhurried. Sometimes a place looked inviting, and they stopped. Sometimes they raced through grey wind-ridden seas, as if their swiftest speed was not enough to satisfy the strength and joy that drove them on.

On that journey the Wanderer saw some colonies of grey seals much bigger than herself. The passing crowd of harp seals looked with mild interest at the antics of their cousins as they sported and hunted fish, but there was no more fraternizing than between different species of birds. The Wanderer recognized similar seals long afterwards when she met them on another side of the world.

One day, after a long sea-journey, the harp herd romped into a bay off a rockbound coast alive with sea-birds. Gannets and skua gulls, kittiwakes and guillemots sailed overhead, their fierce little eyes staring down at the seal-pirates invading their fishing-grounds.

That was the day when the Wanderer showed a younger seal a new game. A cloud of gannets followed a boat pulled by two men, over on the other side of the bay, and the seals could see a board being towed along behind the boat. On this board was painted a herring, and as they watched one bird after another dived to strike, broke its neck hitting the board, and was scooped up into the boat. When the boat had gone big birds were still diving with closed wings deep into the sea to pick out passing fish. The seals swam idly over there to investigate.

One of the gannets, full to the crop with fish, floated, like a little white boat, on the swinging sea. The Wanderer dived, came up beside it, and snapped at it in play—though had she been hungry she might perhaps have caught the bird and dragged it under, drowned it, and eaten it. To her companion the trick was pure joy—the great, convulsive flapping, the red and vengeful look, and the gannet, heavy with gluttony and terror, beating its laborious way up the invisible stairs of the sky.

At about this time the Wanderer's treatment by the great Middle Tribe of the harp seals subtly changed. She was often fretful, looking for a half-remembered companion, and sometimes she pushed unceremoniously among her elders, searching for him. Seals generally keep to their own age-groups, and this intrusion earned her angry looks and snaps.

The fact that she was no longer with one of themselves made the rest of the tribe quicker to resent her. This resurrected her own fear of them, which communicated itself to them, and made them suspicious. She was in that awkward stage between childhood, whose pranks can be ignored, and early adulthood, which may be violent and challenging. The others had the tribal instinct to keep too-young challengers down.

There came a sudden blinding storm of rain after fine weather. The seals played joyously in the rain-pitted waves, but the Wanderer was excluded from the revels, and had to jump and roll by herself. There was a flat calm for a time after the rain ceased. Then a sixty-mile-an-hour gale leapt furiously up and piled the seas high against the shore. The incalculable weight of millions of tons of sea-water thus raised suddenly against the land found some flaw in the basin of the sea-bottom, and at midday, under storm-wracked cloud, there was a convulsive shudder in the ocean, as if the world had cracked.

The submarine earthquake was a small one, or most of the seal-herd would have perished. There was for an instant a waterfall of monstrous size in the midst of the sea as the level adjusted itself to the subsidence of the rock below. Then a wall of water several feet high began to sweep towards the cliffs. Some of the seals were flung far up on the rocks. Others, swimming at top speed against this strange wave, managed to keep offshore, though they were borne far backward.

Smaller waves at intervals glided in the rear of the leader. And then from the deeps below began to float up life that the earthquake had loosed from enormous depths.

The Wanderer scuttered aside in terror as a bearded thing went by, an apparition ten times her own length, with great, flat greenish plates for eyes.

This thing was half-transparent—she could see its internal organs pulsing and swelling and flooding inside the wavering outline. A sort of seaweed beard swept sting-like lashes beneath its head and belly. These black ropes, which looked like tangled plaits of drowned hair, had the power of killing and holding fish that they touched, and then drawing them into a mouth hidden by the beard. At one moment a fish would be darting past in the sea; the next it would be dimly visible in the cloud of the creature's digestive organs, rolling over in a grotesque copy of its movements when alive.

The monster made no sound, and its indeterminate shape and helpless motion offered no evidence of feeling. Yet the sea for many feet around it turned cold with messages of some internal agony.

Very slowly the floating thing began to sink. As it went, from somewhere beneath it floated up groups and strings of bubbles about the size of the Wanderer's head. They had vaguely fishy shapes. Perhaps they were parasitic fish, or roe forced out by the difference in pressure miles up here near the surface, or possibly they were some sort of breath, or even gouts of blood. They burst, leaving nothing but ghostly tinges of colour. For hours afterwards a stench of marsh gas suffused the sea.

15. *The Countless Host*

As the summer advanced the uneasiness of the other seals grew into a tacit hostility towards the Wanderer. It was quietly done, but she soon found herself excluded from all the daily and nightly affairs of the herd. She was allowed to swim only as a sort of solitary camp-follower beyond or behind the rest.

One foggy day a big group of them set off seaward. They took no notice of her following in the distance, so she swam near enough to imitate their communal gambols and gyrations, as if she were still part of their company.

This journey proved to be more than a mere excursion. The group kept steadily on under a soft grey sea-fog that rolled over the waves. Sometimes the seals searched for rosefish. No antagonism was shown when the Wanderer took a place at the end of the far-flung line and helped the others to drive the fish into the centre of a swiftly-tightening circle of hunters. Sometimes they raced on their way, and sometimes dawdled. Now they skimmed the surface, and now shot down through the deeps.

After a long journey they found a new coast ahead and

turned south along it. In summery weather they hurried on. With each day's travel these seals, who had at first tolerated the Wanderer, showed more and more resentment against her. No longer was she allowed to join the fish-hunts or the games. If she came even within a considerable distance of the group the others all flashed away together. Driven off, she followed so far away that once or twice she lost them, and was only able to discover them again by a top-speed search of the seas, which left her almost dead with fatigue.

One evening, as the sun was setting, its low red rays blinded her eyes and made black specks appear that proved, after frantic pursuit, no nearer and no farther away, no more real than at first. The seals had been rounding a great cape that afternoon, and the Wanderer turned north along its farther shore seeking them. She did not know that the others had swung south and west.

They were swimming in a great circle on their way back towards the rest of their tribe. Every frantic beat now carried her farther away from them. She never saw them again.

Tired after a dogged spell of searching, she lay resting on the sea. Through the water from far away came an almost imperceptible throbbing. It increased. After a time a distant speck took the shape of an approaching motor-boat. The Wanderer promptly dived, for she had been attacked by one of these before. The throb of the motor ceased.

After some time of quiet she put her head above the surface to breathe and look round. Instantly there was the bang of a rifle. She dived as a bullet whined off the surface an inch from her head. When she next came up she was a mile away.

The Eskimo leaned out of the drifting boat, his eyes angrily searching down through the water. He was growling savagely at his rifle, abusing it. A primitive Eskimo would have laughed delightedly, unselfish enough to admire the seal's dexterity, and would have hunted on, light of heart. But this man with his motor-boat and rifle had bought anticipation. Half-civilized, and so resentful because machinery fails to bring perfection, he turned his boat about, full of cares.

That experience taught the Wanderer one more of life's lessons. After that if she felt the distant murmur in the water or saw a motor-boat, however far away, she dived at once, and down there out of sight swam to some distant spot. Those who live must learn.

Day by day and night by night she searched for the lost seals of the Middle Tribe. Sometimes she went down to great depths, hoping they might be there. At nights she saw something of the vertical tide of sea-life that flows after the sun has set, when myriads of creatures come swimming upward.

These strangers were of rather darker colour than the mainly silvery inhabitants of the upper waters, and a few of them had phosphorescent lamps in their bodies which they switched on and off at intervals as they dashed along in pursuit or escape. Many were long and eel-like; some had monstrous heads; some were semi-transparent with bones showing through. Some were big, and from them she kept away or actively fled. Some were tiny, and edged out of her path as she approached. But she never found the other seals she was looking for, and gradually forgot them in the new experiences of every adventurous hour.

She hurried on, obeying the first murmur of a command in her blood. Far away across the Polar seas tens of thousands of the seals among whom she had been born were beginning to stir in their annual movement. The instinct to migrate cannot be denied, nor is it understood. As helplessly as the tide sways under the moon, the Wanderer, lost among the islands north of America, obeyed this compulsion to hurry, just as those others did north of Europe. It meant nothing that a great arc of the world lay between them.

The impulse increased as she advanced. The waves seemed to lift her higher as she glided along. Sometimes birds' wings flashed over her, sometimes the whole circle of the moving ocean seemed empty. Occasionally she passed groups of seals different from herself. They looked at her with the same disinterested gaze with which they stared at seaweed floating by.

Once or twice she tried nervously to stay near these strangers. Then their indifference changed to resentment, and in terror she fled away. The power grew that made rest impossible. Her body became frantic to find something her brain knew nothing about. Only swift swimming gave any ease. The water here was too warm, and she missed without knowing it the comfort of the crowded ice. Many weeks passed.

Yet there were glorious days. Once she came unexpectedly on a shoal of fat rose-fish—salmon-red, quick, and exciting. She drove them as a playful dog will drive a mob of chickens, tearing away to head off those who fled, bouncing down over their backs, diving under them to stop them skittering down. Some escaped; the flock dwindled to half a dozen, to three, finally to a solitary one. Growing tired of play, she swooped and bit it across the back. Then she carried it up on to an ice-floe to eat in the sun, unconsciously soothed because sea-ice formations of the type she loved were around her again.

She lazed there for hours, lying almost motionless. She gazed across the swelling sea, closed her eyes in bliss, stared round again, rolling, sun-bathing, scratching. There was something in the air that day that had not been there for weeks—a homeliness after journeying, a deliciously colder feeling in the water.

On the horizon there was a tiny smudge, visible when a far wave lifted, then gone again. With a little choking bark the Wanderer skidded from the floe-edge in a swallow-dive of delight, and began to skim over the sea like a flat stone across a pond.

They were too far off to be identified as seals, and no one can say how she knew they would welcome her when so many other groups had driven her off. Yet when, almost exhausted by her rush to meet them, she floated among the dozen swimming heads the seals greeted her with playful grins and companionably made way for her as she tried to bury her lonely identity in the very midst of their moving pack.

Already, far away where these had come from, she could see another patch of brown. Overcome with excitement, she did not know whether to stay with her first friends or race back to meet the bigger and still more comforting group of newcomers. Those she had joined watched her indecision. They hurried on their way resolutely, their shining heads turning to the stranger, their mermaid eyes gleaming. When she suddenly dived under them, came up far in their rear, and went pelting over the waves to meet the second group, the advanced guard broke into gambols and escapades, their bodies flying like exclamation-marks into the air!

The Wanderer began to behave as if she had inaugurated some splendid game. She swam a little with the second group, aware of a third and still bigger contingent behind. Then she started to play tag, going a little way with each lot and dropping back for the next. She was irresistibly drawn to do so after her long loneliness, because each new swimming regiment was bigger than the last.

All welcomed her. There was never a snap, never that sudden swerve-away of revulsion. First the oncomers swam in dozens or scores. Presently they came in companies of a hundred or so, but later there were ocean-wide assemblies of them. The more there were, the safer she felt and the more delightedly did she dive and twist towards the very middle of the mass.

She had found the third great harp-seal tribe, the western nation of her people, which lives the summer through in the area of the Labrador coasts and Baffin Bay and to an unknown distance farther north.

Now, in early autumn, urged by the migration impulse, they were sweeping south in the Labrador Current—first

in groups, then regiments, and finally in a continuous procession filling the sea as far as the eye could reach. It would
take a whole week for this floating multitude to pass a given
point. They were taking an immemorial trail of their people
over perhaps two thousand miles.

When the Wanderer joined them lanes opened among the
swimmers so that without any choice of hers she found herself presently surrounded by seals of about her own age.
There is usually this age-grouping on migration journeys.
The adults swam together, the two-year adolescents, with
whom she belonged, kept in their own part of the procession,
and the younger cubs had a separate place.

All seals seem happy things, but these two-year-olds,
almost as strong and quick as adults, but without responsi-
bilities, appeared instinct with playfulness. They dashed
aside after imaginary fish, leapt over each other, played
games of ring and tag through the waves.

The host drifting south in the flowing current swung and
separated and rejoined, like floating fields of seaweed. Passing the end of a rugged coastline, they crossed a stretch of
sea, and then began to skirt the high cliffs of a new land.

One day when the Wanderer and some of her friends were
asleep on an ice-floe a lone kyak came waltzing over the sea.
It was steadied and slowed by its occupant, and he crept on
to the far side of the floe and drew up his boat there without
disturbing the sleepers. Then he stole across the ice on hands
and feet, his four-footed walk and furry back giving the
impression of a beast stalking its food.

When he was thirty feet away the seals moved—there
were some flashes in the sunshine and all were gone. Without expression, no more disappointed than if it had come
on to rain, the Eskimo straightened up and walked, a bulky
little figure, back to his kyak. He lifted it into the water,
steadied himself into it, and looked about him for one of the
fugitives to surface. None appeared. Presently, with big
strokes, he drove his leaf-light boat away.

Two or three sunny days were followed by a night of drifting snow. Next morning small puffs as of smoke appeared jumping off the mountain-tops on the distant coast. Loose snow was blowing off the peaks high up there in the sky where an autumn gale was whipping. The puffs increased in frequency. Then, from the upreared white tops came a sudden roaring sound, swiftly stilled. It came again and again, carried on a gusty northern wind. Two or three hours after the first movement of the snow a powerful south-west wind rose suddenly, and for ten minutes blew away the northern gusts that swept across the ice.

Then, as sharply as at the fall of a conductor's baton, the southerly wind was pushed back by a roaring northern blast, so steady and strong that it would have blown a man off his feet. For several hours this yelling wind battered the mountains, flattened the sea, then scooped it into sliding hills, and roared on into the spume-tossed south.

As suddenly as it had come it died away. There was a minute of complete windlessness. The great sea rollers glided silently along under the broken sky. Then a strong and steady north wind broke up the waves anew, and tumbled them into fresh patterns of green and white.

The seals played in the flying water-hills as if they could never have enough of wild movement. As young human animals swoop on skis, as swallows dive with closed wings, and insects almost burst their capsule bodies zooming up a sunbeam, so these seals strove for speed alone.

They flung themselves down the slippery valleys or leaped up into the dissolving tops, so as to be discharged with the avalanche, doubling the utmost natural swiftness of their own torpedo shapes.

The gale broke up some of the newly formed winter ice and flung it about. But as soon as the wind died the ice re-formed in the bays more solidly than before. Overhead there was a steady outrush of wings as the summer birds flew south—divers, mergansers, great flocks of mallard, and

presently the parent gulls. Immature birds of the year were
left, a foolish, shrilling mob, but soon they followed their
elders towards the vanishing sun.

Farther out, where the seals swam, bergs broken from far-
distant glaciers by summer heat were still swinging past in
the current. Many of these icebergs had great fretted arches
in them. As they rode along they looked like ruined cathedrals
—no longer forced to stand neglected and humiliated, but
set adrift upon the sea of time.

The adolescent seals loitered off the mountainous shore,
while the rest of the multitude drifted south past them day by
day. One night, under a moonlit sky, they saw a white bear
sail past on an ice-floe. A solitary and mysterious mariner,
he sat up on his haunches and played a game by whirling
his white paws round and round each other as his ice-ship
bore him out of sight.

The Wanderer seemed by this time to have become one of
the new tribe, as if she had been born in it. She had forgotten the blind yearling, as she had forgotten the mother who
bore her and the painted cub with whom she had played in
the first year of her life. All that had gone, just as yesterday's
rain had vanished from her physical sight. She never thought
about what she should eat, and food was always there to
catch when hunger prompted. The present with its play
and rest filled up the sum of her existence.

The land they were passing looked deserted now that
winter was closing in. Yet eyes watched the seals sometimes
from those forbidding cliffs. One day, when the youngsters
were skimming to and fro in the mouth of a bay, two fur-clad
men came climbing out over the ice forming against the
shore. A snowfall had caused new black ice, which was very
thin and slippery in places. It undulated as the men advanced, and they began to trot so as not to leave their weight
dangerously long on one foot.

After running for some distance they stopped where the
ice was fairly thick. There they squatted down and began

to cut away the surface with ice-chisels, sending opaque chips flying. One hole was only a few inches wide. The other, close to it, was rather bigger.

One man with a harpoon on a very long pole stood over the small hole, pointing his weapon down it. The other lay face down on the ice and drew a sealskin over his head, with just a crack open in front of his eyes. Staring down into the sea under the hole he made whistling noises, and then a long-drawn bubbling sound like a seal's cry. Meanwhile his friend cautiously lowered the tip of the harpoon down the narrower hole. Attached to its end by a thong was a spinner carved like a fish, and this he skilfully played so that it whirled and flickered in the water.

With tireless endurance they continued their decoy work hour after hour.

Late in the afternoon the Wanderer saw in the distance that appetizing flash as the spinner turned in the clear green water. She shot along under the ice to examine it, attracted the more by a few succulent white shrimps swimming round it. It moved like a fish, it was shaped like a delicate little white fish. Gliding under the ice, she swam up to look at the tantalizing thing more closely.

Glancing up through a hole, she saw what she thought was a seal's head and heard a seal's cry. Then, as he saw her body pass towards the narrower hole, the watcher grunted a command, and the man with the long harpoon stabbed savagely down.

16. Nightmare Net

As the Wanderer kicked sideways at the sound of the man's command, the harpoon cut across her shoulder, instead of piercing deep in her back. The point glanced off, and she raced away with a bleeding weal in her fur. Her terrified flight from under the ice scattered the rest of the seal-youngsters, and they tore out of the bay southward in the track of their tribe.

The two hunters back on the ice got up, flexed their cramped muscles, and set off wearily homeward. They were not disheartened. They would try somewhere else to-morrow and very likely make a catch. They were talking cheerily before they had gone many yards from their abandoned holes, where the Wanderer's body might by that time have been lying half skinned. But she was miles away in the sea, her shoulders thrilling with pain. She was stiff for a few days afterwards, but then the cut healed.

She found herself accepted in a group of half a dozen two-year-olds, led by one whose back showed the parallel scars of a bear's claws, by which he had been raked long ago. These youngsters were prankish, curious, and vigorous. They

rushed up and down the waves, or dived to pop up a whiskered face in front of some sedate fellow-traveller. While the
others drifted along in the strong current these young ones
tore aside into every bay, revelling in the novelties of the
water with its exciting new tastes and smells and rippling
lifts.

These new friends were eager hunters, and they taught
the Wanderer all sorts of tricks and pursued with her many
fishes she had not yet become adept at catching. The greeny-
silver scintillation of great cod-shoals fled away before them.
Most of the cod were half the length of the Wanderer, but
some of the big old leaders were nearly as large as herself.

They jittered away when the seals dashed after them, but
let them glide never so fast or twist never so swiftly, they
could not match the dancing shadows which pursued them.
Presently came the glorious slash across that sheeny olive
back, the convulsive thumpings and shudderings thrilling
the enclosing jaws, the dragging of the flopping, bleeding
victim on to an ice-floe, and a meal from the belly and
tenderest parts, the rest being left for any scavenger of the
air or sea who wanted it. Then the chase was taken up anew
for nothing more than the sensuous savagery of pursuit.

It was the bear-marked two-year-old who taught the
Wanderer that she had a palate—that black coal-fish, almost
as big as a large cod, had more flavour, and offered more
excitement in the chase. The cod dived and zoomed through
the sea. But the coal-fish turned cunningly into shallow
water, and would escape at the final moment by casting
itself up on the beach. Then the defeated seal would glide
swiftly out to sea, and sometimes the flopping victim would
manage to convulse itself back into water and life again.

The bear-marked seal showed the Wanderer exactly where
to circle like a streak and head the fugitive off from the
shallows. This was a sport among equals, for if the seal
circled too many times the coal-fish might tire it at last and
shake it off, whereas direct chase sent it up the beach, and

I

that was no good either. Perhaps the extra energy consumed in catching these black slithering beauties made them taste more ravishing, or perhaps the seal-muscles exulted in being driven to the furthest limits of power and skill. At least when a coal-fish was gripped the whole of life seemed suddenly to reach perfection.

Sometimes there were herrings to eat, and sometimes small cuttlefish, sometimes whitefish or capelin or clione, but, more often by far, sweet little crustaceans. As the seal-host poured along they swept the seas of food; there are experts who say that over two hundred million cod alone are taken by seals off this coast every year.

Sometimes they themselves suffered sudden alarms. During a night of snow the Wanderer was passed by several far bigger, powerful, sturgeon-like creatures going hard south.

Then there was an evening under an icy sunset when an endless worm-like nemertine, far bigger than the biggest harp seal, came undulating out of the scarlet west and cut a path through the swimming multitude. It was of a green colour, blind, perhaps, but with lateral slits in its head, and fin-like membranes, by which it helped to wriggle itself along. It had a voracious look, though it seemed unaware of the thousands of seals who fell over each other to open a path. As it went it stooped suddenly deep and came up again with some struggling creature of considerable size slowly being enclosed in its distended mouth. It swam undulating on, rolling its prey over and over while trying to force it in, gulping and slavering, and after the still-live mass had been been fully surrounded, it could be seen slowly shuddering as it was crammed inch by inch along the monster's gullet.

During this journey the travellers one day came upon two leviathan forms floating across the seal-path south. It was a whale-mother at the surface, suckling her baby at a teat in a groove near the root of her mighty tail, itself three times the Wanderer's length. The mother, whose mouth looked big enough to engulf innumerable seals, wallowed modestly, a mild monstrosity of affection, careful not to displace her offspring. Meanwhile the young one, half as large as its overwhelming parent, clung, by means of a mouth like a sea cave, immediately under the overshadowing flukes, and swallowed without ceasing such cataracts of milk as might have poured over a white Niagara.

The Wanderer, diving away below, saw great white spots on an underbelly grooved like the boards of a ship, ear-like fins bigger than herself, and the shining eye of the suckling frowning with concentration upon its task as its body swayed to and fro. Then the two colossi, startled without cause, were gone, leaving the water above heaving and seals gushing up and down in a stupendous turbulence.

The current swept them along at several knots, and excitement spread through the herd as the southern destination was swiftly approached. Diving deep after fish, or riding the swaying floes, the seals lived in an idyllic communal tranquillity.

Yet, as always, death swam invisible among them. Sometimes a white bear, sometimes a killer whale, and sometimes man struck swiftly here or there. Every week the number of the moving multitude was lessened.

The Wanderer, with her little group, came to an ice-edged bay, and they plunged into it full of excitement to taste and smell and feel and see and hear. The rolling water crashed over their backs, there was a place between two crab-claw headlands that promised fish, and they rollicked into it.

Bang!

The claw-marked seal rolled over as if he had been kicked. A thin stream of blood curled and floated away from his ear, and he began to sink as the dead sink, while a puff of smoke detached itself from the rocks, and a man holding a rifle appeared, jumping towards the water.

The rest of the seals were already skimming away deep under the surface like great shadows. The Wanderer fled faster than any, but as nothing pursued she soon lost her

urgency. Half an hour later she was exploring a twirling
current of water that flowed under the waves from the edge
of the land. This water bore with it strange smells, dark
clouds of mud, and then suddenly a spinning mob of little
silvery-scaled whitefish, like fluttering butterflies of the sea.

She sideslipped after them, following first one and then
another, dived to send one zooming up, then towered over
it and forced it down flying for its life. Curving her body to
follow its glittering turns, she reached forward to snap at it
—and felt something coarse and hard scrape her nose. She
did a backward somersault in the water to escape that terrifying touch. As she sped away another black coil striped across
her face and made her redouble on her own tracks.

She had blundered into a rope-net. Its rough tentacles
drove her in and clutched her first on this side, then on that.
From skilled instinctive doublings to escape, she fell into
panic-stricken blunderings and convulsive leapings.

The tarry monster that enclosed her was in no hurry to
complete its work. It was alarming to her, because it was
unnatural. It followed no animal order of attack. It did not
bite or rip or swallow. It coldly hemmed her round with a
cobweb of swimming, horribly yielding, yet utterly imprison-
ing, ropes.

The most gentle of creatures, the Wanderer was now so
frightened that terror made her fierce. She bit at the ropes.
But they dragged and sawed across her delicate mouth with
the leapings of her body and the sway of the sea, tearing her
lips till they bled, and making her back away, spitting. One
flipper caught in a mesh of the net and was agonizingly
twisted. She struggled to fight it loose.

She made an all-out dart, only to be thrown backward by
a blow in the face as the net tautened sharply. She dived,
and was bagged in a sagging pocket which enfolded her
round, and for a ghastly minute stomached her as if she had
been swallowed alive. Jerking out of it by spasmodic hops,
unnatural to a swimming creature, she raced on upward,

only to find the whole top of the net narrowing, thickening, tightening.

It was being drawn, jerk by jerk, up through the water.

In redoubled panic she fought the closing ropes.

Then, when most of all she needed strength, her vision shimmered like a falling wave, her muscles sagged, and she floated helpless in the bottom of the net.

She had been underwater too long. The oxygen in her blood was used up. Her strength was gone, and there remained only a few moments before she would be hauled into the air like an old soggy coat in a string-bag.

A convoy of white shrimps, fiercely driving their tiny paddles, darted through the rope squares of the net, and trod water just above her closed eyes. By an irony of nature, though seals eat live shrimps, shrimps eat dead seals. Avidly waiting, they danced in the water with twitching limbs.

17. *World under the Waves*

As the net, dripping like a bundle of snakes, was hauled to the sea surface, the Wanderer drew two or three deep and rapid breaths.

Life flowed from them suddenly into her limp body; she saw a two-legged animal, assisted by another, drawing her up, and she turned and flashed against the side of the net before anyone realized she was alive. Floating loose no longer, but held taut by the hands of the man above, the tarred cords snapped into rotted fibres, and one of the men gave a shout of anger as the seal burst out of the net and slid down through the sea.

She had escaped from such two-legged creatures before, but she had never been so close to them, never felt helplessly bound, never suffered such hurt at their hands. Above all, she had never before heard one of them make any loud cry. That explosive yell of enmity only a foot or two from her sensitive ears burned a terror of men on her fleeting memory. For weeks afterwards, when some movement or sound awoke her sense of fear, though her mind was incapable of remembering the details of her escape, she heard that shout again.

The great company of migrating seals felt the sway of excitement increasing as they drew near their journey's end. At Belle Isle Strait, north of Newfoundland, they fanned out into two swimming fleets. One fleet verged westward, while the other swept along the coast of the island and away out towards the Grand Bank. With these went the Wanderer, still chastened and timid from her death-struggle with the net. For a while she avoided all curiosities and adventures, and travelled quietly through the vastness of the wintry sea.

Driven before the seals went the flickering hosts of cod. And now, as they approached the undersea plateau that extends for five hundred miles into the Atlantic south-east of Newfoundland, the seals found great shoals of other fish.

The Wanderer had never before seen such a wonderland as this. The top of the Grand Bank was here only five or six hundred feet under the waves, and sunlight could penetrate far down and stimulate a profusion of marine creation.

Her new timidity could not survive among such fascinations as these. Diving down, she constantly peered at the variety of shells and floating tailless heads, blindworms and weird-eyed fish, unidentified silvery flashes and dark passing masses, not one of which could be spied on without alertness in case it suddenly threatened death.

Once, when heavy fog rolling above made the depths very dark, she passed a host of phosphorescent atomies, like stars in a clear sky, emitting a scintillating light, now increasing and now decreasing in intensity. Perhaps these tiny things had been chased from the deeps to the top of the banks, for just after they had passed came a number of creatures with organs in their heads which produced dull bubbles of light, which flared and were extinguished and abruptly flared again. She slipped swiftly away to one side, for the pursuing lights had a deadly look of purpose as they hurried on the trail of the sea-stars.

While she was lazily gliding upside down not far over the sunken hills, a slim fish, hardly a foot long, passed over her.

Trailing from its tail and under-fins were three string-like rays, longer than the fish's body, one of which touched the Wanderer's fore-flipper floating by. She felt as if she had been hit again by the Eskimo's harpoon, and fled away at the top of her speed. At the contact the small fish turned its blind head and looked at her, but made no effort to follow. For days there remained a tiny scar which burned and shot pain through the flipper that had been touched.

Once, though the seals felt no disturbance of the water where they played and dived, there must have been some commotion in a crevasse of the undersea plateau. For on an icy up-current came thousands of dead and dying fish of a kind the seals had never seen before, bony shapes with spiky backs and lantern-jawed heads. They floated up in a spreading mass. They were not wounded, and showed no marks of disease or parasites. Yet those not dead already gasped and died as they came up, and within a minute they lost the elasticity and iridescence of life, and turned black and slimy as well as limp.

Round them, arriving in swiftly-increasing numbers, came a variety of higher-level fishes, dashing to and fro as they ate their way into this cloud of manna ascending from below instead of falling from above.

The voraciousness of the creatures of this world below the waves was often in inverse ratio to their size. The seals biting into the vitals of a leaping fish looked almost gentle by comparison with some of these smaller killers.

There were some dark little fish not more than three inches long, which lurked about the sunken hilltops. They were smooth, streamlined, shapely, with round and cheerful eyes. Yet when they opened their long mouths they showed appalling backward-growing teeth. They not merely attacked other creatures, but incessantly pursued each other in a catch-as-catch-can; irrespective of size, one would grip in its jaws, by a sudden convulsion, the head of one of its own kind, almost half as large again as itself, pierce through it with killing teeth, and then slowly swallow it down. The victim would be forced into the attacker's abdomen unbroken, and lie curled there, dead. Meanwhile the conqueror, its distended belly hanging down three times its own depth and most of its own length, would feebly swim about, opening and shutting its awful mouth, physically incapable of overtaking or containing anything else, but making constant snapping motions, as if nothing could ever stop its appetite.

In places where, by deep and prolonged dives, the Wanderer could approach the tops of the underwater hills, the water was often so clouded with floating matter that she did not swim into it. She often approached these obscurities, only to skitter away in terror.

Creatures lurked in and stirred up these clouds of ooze. Sometimes as she peered, her sensitive recording-hairs quivering with unreadable messages from the mists, vast disturbances took place there, sending clouds puffing outward—hidden fights, love-makings, killings, escapes, and pursuits.

Some of the things that slid in and out seemed to be midway between animals and plants. They looked like carrots, with a dull-reddish pointed body, above which waved a cluster of indented tentacles. But these creatures had eyes—large bulbous eyes, one on each side where tentacles and 'root' met—and something capable of the differing focuses of greed and fear looked through those eyes as the oddity floated by.

There were nightmare shrimps, big and little, hunting each other, and things like swimming tree-roots with snaky muscular trunks that bent and searched.

Very few of these creatures ever came near the surface of the sea; they lived in their world as we live in ours, as unfamiliar with the earth's sunny exterior as we are with these watery wrinkles in its skin. The coldness of that primordial world, with its foggy darkness, insatiable appetites, and monstrous shapes was home to them.

Once the Wanderer was suddenly enveloped in a cloud of ooze, bursting up from the depths like the smoke of an explosion. In its midst swirled an old sperm-whale ten times her own length, shaped as if he had been beheaded and left truncated. Through the fog she saw that he had a giant squid in his grip.

The whale had been hunting through the undersea clouds, and perhaps had torn the squid from some hiding-place, or come upon it as it floated free. The cavernous whale-jaw had opened, one of the squid's arms was seized and chopped by conical teeth weighing several pounds apiece, and the victim had instantly leapt to the offensive. Round the whale's head lashed the squid's thirty-foot arms, ropes of corded muscle, each equipped with rows of suckers strengthened by horny rings. Even in the tough whale-skin these suckers sank toothed circles inches across. Having thus made its mighty grasp secure, the squid tried as it was whirled up through the water to feel for some vulnerable organ.

The whale thrashed and struggled, biting his way along the immense arm held in his mouth. He was fighting to bring his jaws across the squid's visceral sac, out of which the monster's frightful eyes stared in agony. But the squid, finding nothing but coarse skin on which to vent its strength, shifted its grip. One endless tentacle flared across the attacker's head, feeling for a tongue, an ear, a soft defenceless eye.

With a whirl like a herring, the fifty-ton whale rolled round in the sea and dodged again and again that blinding grip. Working his jaws to smash and chew through the tentacle, hard as a rubber tree-trunk, he tried by brute strength to drag the monstrous suckers out of their rooted penetration of his head and so force the vulnerable body round where he could bite on it.

With a sudden shift the squid got a grip right across the whale's eye-ridge. As if that arm could now see the vital spot, several more began to writhe across the smooth head

towards the eye. Even the ripped tentacle in the whale's
jaw tried convulsively to drag itself out and join the attack,
while the squid's horny, parrot-like beak protruding from the
circlet of arms erected itself and gaped, ready to receive
whatever might be torn out.

Still fighting in the sea-clouds, the combatants rolled over
and over in their gargantuan wrestle, the armless against the
ten-armed, the biter against the gouger. Inch by inch, the
first tentacle's extremity, where a group of suckers concen-
trated into a sort of nailed fist, hopped nearer the whale's eye.

The squid's haste to kill betrayed it. For an instant, seeking a closer hold, the terrible suckers were loosened a little
—and with a mighty jerk of the head the whale dragged the
whole bag of the victim's body into his teeth. There was a
ghastly sound, the water round darkened with inky gouts of
blood, and frantic tentacles whipped about. Then the remaining arms fell loose, and the whole creature began to
jerk yard by yard down the whale's throat.

It was eaten—legs, body, beak, and all. But the sperm-
whale had not escaped unscathed. Round his jaws and up
across his head were long rows of parallel weals an inch or
two across, tooth-marked and deep. One of those awful
stripes ran within an inch of his eye. They would leave scars
if he lived for a hundred years.

The Wanderer was gone. When titans struggle in the
deeps all lesser creatures flee away. For a quarter of a mile
around the whale as he circled slowly and victoriously among
the dead squid's dissipating ink there was not a fish, not a
crab, not a shrimp; and away below his heavy belly the
clouds of the ooze rolled cold and deserted in the dark.

18. Jewelled Nursery

THE seals, who had played so happily for a month over the top of the Grand Bank, again grew restless. All day heads popped out of the waves and stared at each other, while fog diamonded their whiskers.

The Wanderer lost her urge to trespass in the watery underworld. The whole tossing area of the wintry sea, which they had swum two thousand miles to reach, now seemed strange. They all began to look towards the north, from which they had come.

One day a few scores of the adult females started to swim into the north. They were ten-months heavy with babies almost due to be born, yet they slipped through the sea with a sleek, unfailing grace. They seemed to swim more easily and leisurely, swaying in pretty glides over the wave-crests.

As the gleaming heads drew away across the water hundreds more took up travelling places and began to follow. Before evening all the pregnant adults had gone. The rest of the herd moved about uneasily. In the dawn on the following day the adult males set off northward in a huge, swift-swimming regiment.

Away they went, fading presently out of sight, while the youngsters stared at each other at being left alone. Then the Wanderer and a few more, the best-built and most mature among these adolescents, felt suddenly that they must turn north too. They scudded through the tops of the waves, and behind them swept all the remainder of the host which had come south. By that evening the cod-shoals discovered a new freedom.

On that first day of return along the sea-road the Wanderer recognized an iceberg she had seen months before. It was a pinnacled monster, with three great ice-arches one behind the other, tilting and drifting south in the current against which the travellers were swimming. Seals have considerable visual memory, and she darted away from the rest and circled happily round the fantastic ship of ice, standing with her shoulders out of the water two or three times to look at it. She only abandoned it when the last stragglers were almost out of sight. Then with speed she overtook and passed them, racing on until she was up in the van of the youngsters again.

Such bergs sometimes swirl for weeks in some eddy of an ocean current while their companions sail past, often veiled in fog caused by the impact of warmer air on their own icy breath.

By day and night the young seals hurried on. They swam north because they had to, because the throb of blood in their veins moved their flippers to push the sea under them away to the south. As they went, the compulsion that drew them grew stronger.

During one night as they swam north the Wanderer heard from far across the waves the ghost of a sound. It was a sound she had heard a year ago as she swam, a solitary stray, towards the Middle Tribe of the harp seals a quarter of the world away near Jan Mayen.

Perhaps because in her lonely state this far-away wailing had so deeply moved her then, she became almost frantically

excited now. Her hind-limbs began to beat the water at
racing speed. Each foot, every one of the five long toes on
each, seemed separately to push harder than ever in her life
before. She shot out ahead of the others. The sea bubbled
past and under her as she slid her head and part of her chest
over the surface.

As she went, pursued by a few others infected by her
excitement, the wailing of hungry seal-babies two miles away
was suddenly brought more clearly by a puff of wind across
the sea. Skimming the surface swift as a skater, she rushed
on under the radiance of a great full moon. It brushed her
back with silver, topped the waves with silver, and set white
fire to the spray out-flung by her head.

Suddenly she saw ahead a wonderland. Faintly moving
ice-floes stretched in a half-circle from horizon to horizon.
They were sugared with new snow, and the angle of the
setting moon made each one glisten and sparkle.

On the nearer floes the Wanderer could see the first of the
white seal-babies, round as little snowmen and as soft as love.
Each with infinitely appealing black eyes and a little black
blotch of nose, they sprawled crying for the warmth and
comfort their mouths would draw from their mothers' very
hearts.

The sight of this nursery released in the Wanderer's body
a new feeling. She was already almost mature in shape and
size, precociously rounded and strengthened by travels half-
encircling the northern world. In a year she would taste
the thrill and pain of her first mating, and conceive one of
these furry bundles that cried so urgently to her or any
feminine thing.

Though her brain could not anticipate, her body throbbed
with recognition as she climbed on to the nearest floe and
looked searchingly at the white babies on their counterpane
of snow.

She looked round the moon-blue birthplace fashioned by
nature with sea-foam curtains and starlight stairs. The waves

rocked the cradles of ice and lipped at their edges, whispering an ocean lullaby.

In the dawn when the sun rose fiery through a sea-fog a refraction of the light for a few minutes changed the nursery snow-crystals to rubies. These faded, became colourless, and then, directly lighted by the rising sun, began to blaze in a diamond sparkle.

While Nature changed her jewels, whitecoat babies crawled about uttering hungry cries. Their mothers fed them each morning and evening, and often during the day as well. At other times the mothers slept on the floes, the cubs tucked into their sides. Sometimes a seal-mother would sleep on her back with flippers spread out, showing her soft, velvet throat. Then her baby would ridiculously imitate her attitude, getting with difficulty on its milk-rounded back and trying to stretch out in desperate peril of rolling on to its side. Too uneasy to sleep, because of this difficulty of balance, it would nervously brush its throat or try to wash its face, and always end by helplessly capsizing.

Overwhelmed at the difficulties of life, the white baby would cry in a high-pitched voice, at which the mother would not even open an eye. It would shake its head with an absurd appearance of self-pity, shed tears, and wipe its eyes with flat little flippers.

Defying neglect, it would crawl off, play with another cub, try bravely to creep up a little hummock of ice, and slide back a dozen times on its bottom.

Finally it would scramble a foot or two up this ascent perilous, and then—betrayed yet again by its infantile rotundity—simply roll down and bump its black nose painfully.

At that it would shriek in earnest, and its playmates would shriek even louder. A sleek and lovely head would raise itself here or there and give a placid maternal look and sink again in gentleness to sleep. The bawling would suddenly stop. Then some of the other white babies who had been onlookers would assault the three-foot ice-mountain with appalling ferocity or globular cunning—according to their natures, or perhaps even as a distinction of sex.

These ice-hummocks, besides being monsters to be fought or playmates to be cuffed and snarled at, were often pressed into service as protectors during the hours that the mother was away swimming. Then the little whitecoat would snuggle himself close against the inanimate side, where hurrying adults could not tread on him, roll on to his back with the ice's valuable support, fold his flipper hands on his breast with an ineffable air of virtue, and sleep for hours, making now and then tiny authoritative gestures.

The Wanderer watched the whitecoats intently whenever she could do so without angering their mothers. Floating for hours in the water, she observed their every movement. Often when the mothers were away she climbed out on to a floe, though she never touched the babies as they gambolled round.

Sometimes she would support herself with her fore-flippers on the edge of a piece of ice, with only her nose and eyes above the surface, tirelessly watching. The whitecoats waddled about, the seal-mothers fed them or swam, the splendid old harp-marked males splashed in the water. The jewelled nursery seemed a place of peace and unshadowed happiness in that wonderland of ice.

One day there came humming and roaring overhead something greater than any bird, something whose metallic wings shone in the sun. It circled the whole expanse of the seal-nursery two or three times, and then faded away in the direction from which it had come.

Next morning the seals were startled by half a dozen two-legged creatures walking towards them over the ice. These men crossed water-leads by leaping from ice-pan to ice-pan, and carried on their backs big rucksacks. The Wanderer saw them coming, and she and every grown seal slithered swiftly off the floes into the sea. She circled away in deep water, but after a few minutes curiosity forced her to rise and stare at the invaders.

The men had set up a small folding-table, and some of them were heating branding-irons with a blowlamp while others walked about collecting baby seals. Some of these crawled away, but others lay down, pressing their fore-flippers close to their bodies and drawing their heads under the elastic blubber-lined skin of the neck instinctively to form a bolster over the skull. They then shut their eyes, and made no movement when touched or picked up.

The men laughed aloud at them, called, and pointed. Then they rolled or dragged the unresisting bodies along the ice, or picked them up and carried them under one arm to the operating-table. Once the three-foot-six whitecoat was laid on the table it would remain there immobile for a moment, and then shyly open its eyes and glance up to see what was happening.

While one man held it firmly another would press a red-hot branding-iron for a few seconds into the thick white fur on the back of the neck, pushing it to and fro to clear away charred fur, and finally scorching to a light brown a clean area of skin half as big as the palm of a man's hand.

Sometimes a whitecoat would permit this without complaint. Another would hiss and snap, and be given a light, almost friendly, cuff on the nose, at which first lesson that there is cruelty in the world, it would sink down and struggle no more. It was certainly not hurt, and showed no sign at all of being badly frightened.

The branding over, while one man entered notes of identity in a book, another took a stainless-steel metal tag with a number punched on it and clinched it permanently to the whitecoat's flipper margin. Rarely did a drop of blood appear. The whole operation took only a few minutes. Finally, the furry baby was lifted from the table, carried thirty or forty paces away, and set free in the snow.

Several of the little white victims of man's desire to know lolloped back towards the operating-table and crowded under the feet of the two-legged creatures who had thus strangely

K

used them. The men bawled with laughter at first. Then they grew annoyed, after almost falling headlong once or twice, and the marked whitecoats were shoved unceremoniously out of the way with a booted foot.

Having marked all the babies on that floe, the operators moved on and began work on the next. Dozens of cubs were branded and numbered that day, while the agitated mothers swam swiftly about in the water-leads, surfacing and staring, diving out of sight and flashing to and fro under water. They were too terrified to climb up on the floes or make any effort to defend their babies, who by this time were shrieking their hunger to the placid springtime sky.

Presently when the men were a good way off a seal slithered up on the ice, then another, and another. They suckled their cubs in alarm, then dashed back into the sea. They did not seem to fear the burnt-fur smell, or shrink from the strange new markings or the gleaming metal tags. As for the youngsters themselves, in their milky-whiskered orgies, they seemed to have forgotten all they had been through.

The scientists were branding these cubs so that hunters killing whitecoats should avoid them. Later, whenever an adult seal was killed, it was hoped that the metal disc would be returned, in exchange for a small reward, to the scientific institute whose address it bore. In that way it would be possible to learn something about the movements of these seals born up here in the ice, north of Newfoundland, how and where they wandered, and to make some guesses at the unsolved mysteries of their lives. It is from such threads of evidence that some of the adventures here have come to be written.

The Wanderer, when at last she dared to go back to the floe where she usually rested, was stirred by a new excitement. She no longer remembered the painted cub she had swum with for the first year of her life. Yet the markings and the bright metal tabs on the whitecoats roused emotions in her, and she hurried from cub to cub, looking searchingly at each as if to discover something. Once or twice alarmed mothers turned fiercely on her and she dodged away.

The whole community of seals was agitated by this human invasion. Males and females lifted their heads incessantly. Swimmers darted to the surface and stared about, dived as if escaping, and clambered on to the floes only after nervous peering on every side.

The fat little whitecoats, marked and unmarked alike, played as happily as before. They had not been hurt, and they were innocent of fear.

But through the icy seas a little to the south a hunter was steaming towards them vaster than any whale, more dangerous than the cruellest shark.

19. Red Day

A FEW days had passed since the scientists came, and the disturbance they caused had subsided. Most of the births were now completed, and only one or two animals still remained pregnant.

The weather, which had been so sunny and fine, was breaking up. Yesterday was filled with sullen cloud while a shrill wind agitated the sea between the ice and sent it slapping in bursts of foam. This was weather the seals revelled in, and swimmers played by hundreds wherever narrow currents between promontories gathered the broken water into eddies. The sky steadily darkened with a bruised, greenish look.

At first the distant smudge of smoke seemed no more than a thicker cloud. But it hung persistently in the sky to the south, and presently imperceptibly came nearer to the jewelled nursery. An eight-year-old male, grey-white, powerful, with a black harp-mark across his back, suddenly lifted his head and stared. He could hear or feel through the ice a faint intermittent vibration, something too harsh to belong to the movements of waves and wind.

Others round him stiffened into attitudes of listening. The din of the cubs instinctively stilled. The old seal arched his body, hauled his rear forward, and pushed jerkily ahead towards the end of the floe. At the water's edge he paused, staring in the direction of the distant stain in the sky. Then he slid into the water and disappeared. Others began to do the same. They did not hurry. They were not much alarmed, but they felt more at ease in the sea than on the ice.

The jarring continued. The smoke spread closer. After some time there appeared far away a black dot on the white. It was moving—breaking and bursting its way slowly nearer.

A single funnel belched smoke heavily. The steel colossus hit the ice with a thunderous roar, sending water high from its armoured bow. Long cracks shot out through the ice in every direction. The bow climbed slightly on to the ice, then backed a little to give itself impetus to smash forward again. Masts like giant antennæ stuck up fore and aft. High on one of them was a white cage, and from it the black head and shoulders of a man appeared, studying the ice ahead and shouting information.

At this apparition, though it was still a good way off, most of the grown seals plunged from the floes into the safety of the sea. A few mothers remained on the ice, impatiently suckling their babies or creeping about in jerky alarm.

The invading monster smashed its way nearer. It seemed to climb forward on the ice, using all its weight to bear down and crack open a passage. Other than that it made no alarming gesture. The swimming seals watched it as much in curiosity as alarm.

Suddenly the ship hesitated in its forward rush at the ice and shuddered through its whole length. Men's voices bawled, and its progress was halted. It lay there in the lane it had cut, smoking furiously. Its propeller had struck a large loose block of ice. Damage had been done. The propeller was enclosed in a steel frame so that, in case of breakage, this frame could be detached from the shaft, raised, a new propeller fixed, and the whole lowered into place again.

Now the captain and the engineer debated, while crowds of men stood impatiently about the decks and pointed to the distant seals. The engineer advised withdrawal into open water, and a full-scale repair. But the captain had his duty to his owners for a profitable voyage. Tantalizingly within reach was a great colony of whitecoats whose skins he had come to fetch.

He stared into the threatening sky and listened to the rising shrillness of the wind. A storm was coming. It would pile ice here so that he would not be able to force his ship in again. A day's delay now would rob him of everything. Was it possible to get their hides off them first, then retreat to the safety of the open water far behind? Could it be done before the gale brought floes to shut him in? Such daily decisions are the perilous stuff on which the seal-fur trade is based.

The captain abruptly made up his mind. His ship was not crippled, only a little weakened. He spoke to the engineer, who looked up sharply, half-opened his mouth to speak, then decided to obey without question. Sealer captains are hard men. They do not tolerate comments on their orders. A moment later the steel monster appeared to utter a chattering cry. The men on the decks were cheering the decision to kill.

They began handing out long sticks ending in pointed iron gaffs, a sort of combination boat-hook and spear about five feet long. Orders were shouted. Then two or three score of men began to go overside on to the ice and divide up into parties. They wore knee-boots, warm clothes that made them look fat, gloves, and caps. One or two, the dandies among them, had sealskin-fur hats.

Stringing out into lines, they began to clink across the ice towards various parts of the seal-colony. They walked carefully, the leaders testing the way with their poles.

Drifted snow may cover a fissure between floes, and it is not the way to begin a day's hunting in that killing ice-wind by getting wet through. As they went they shouted cheerful gibes and burst into laughter.

The Wanderer had long ago fled into the water. As the men approached, all but two of the remaining grown seals dived. The leading man of the line scuffling towards that floe raised a rifle. It banged once—again—again. A seal-mother sprawled helplessly beside her cub. Too young to be afraid at her collapse, it bustled forward greedily to suckle. The other shot adult was the last of the pregnant mothers, now within an hour of giving birth. She had been hit twice, and lay moving feebly, dying.

The men on the floe separated into pairs and began systematically and silently to work. The first man, holding his gaff in both hands, thudded it into the head of a whitecoat baby. Then another. Then another. One blow expertly delivered was usually enough to kill without badly tearing the fur. The little white creatures made no effort to escape, and seemed to have no fear of what was happening.

As the killer moved methodically among them his mate skinned the seal-babies with expert swiftness—a knife-rip, one violent pull, and the pelt was off like an overcoat. He threaded it on to a line that trailed over his shoulder and dragged behind him across the ice. Another slash and the liver was hooked on the belt the man wore around his waist. Fresh whitecoat livers are said by these seamen to be an epicure's tit-bit such as no costly restaurant can equal. The skinner skilfully left one front flipper in each pelt. Some of these dainty flippers would be eaten by the ship's crew. The rest would be sold as delicacies on returning to port, and the money by ancient custom divided between the seamen.

The killer suddenly stopped his swinging weapon in mid-air and swore savagely. The whitecoat crawling between his booted feet was marked with a scientist's branding-iron, a red splotch among the pure white fur. He kicked the cub

aside, passed to the next, and found it marked too. He
turned to his mate with a burst of blasphemy. In the hectic
pace of killing, these seal-babies must be conspicuously
marked or discovery comes too late. The spared whitecoats
trundled away on some concern of their own.

The killer paused and wiped the sweat from his forehead.
He and his mate bent over the pregnant seal they had shot.
A few grunted words, and the two men began to work
rapidly together. First they flayed the mother. Then they
ripped open her belly, pulled out the unborn baby, stripped
it too, jerked out its liver, and left the remnants in a steaming
heap.

As soon as the sealers began to trail out in dark lines over
the ice from their ship ivory gulls had come gliding up overhead, their beautiful white plumage relieved only by the
sharp black spots of their eyes and beaks. When the flaying
began the birds queued up on the ice, like women at the
butcher's. As the skinned carcases were abandoned they
leapt upon them, ripping off and swallowing long shreds of
flesh that had hardly ceased to quiver.

Often they could not control their impatience long enough
to wait until the lightning operation of the flaying was done.
They would hop forward and nervously peck at one side of
the body before the uncaring skinner had finished work on
the other. When a big glaucous gull came sailing down the
ivory gulls edged uncomfortably away to make room for it.
On the water in the leads fulmars savagely fought each other
for blood and blubber spilled and floating there.

As the two men stepped forward to recommence the
slaughter a desperate seal-mother landed swiftly ahead of
them. Advancing with a kind of undulatory gallop at a
speed that would have outstripped for a short distance a
man running, she rushed to her cub and tried to nose it into
the water. As the sealers ran at her, she did something harp
seals hardly ever dare to do—turned on them open-mouthed.
In a moment she was stabbed to death and her cub was

rolling dead beside her, but the skinner was spitting out oaths and hopping and holding his leg. Her teeth had snapped clean through his stout boot and torn out a big piece of his calf. He limped, but he could still work. Swearing savagely, he flayed the two victims. Then he hopped along after his mate, rip-rip-ripping at the growing lines of the dead.

Suddenly the clouds seemed to thrust down, as if to throw a pall over this red smudging of the virgin ice. In the sudden darkening, white faces everywhere turned abruptly up. Then some of the older men looked expectantly towards the ship. With a shriek a long gust of wind cut over the floes like a greater skinning-knife. The men began again faster than ever to move forward the scarlet lines of death.

Some animals kill for food and some for pleasure. Only the human animal slaughters wholesale for profit. The seal-babies were selected because women want their pretty skins. Whitecoat fur is used, either plain or dyed in various colours, over much of the world. Most of the skins are processed in London. Young harp-seal furs are sold in their natural colour, or dyed in ocelot, beaver, and mink colours. As well as for furs, they are used for bootees, girls' sports-coats, and for many trimmings. Older animals' skins are used as leather for a thousand everyday purposes, while other parts of their bodies are in various places made into soaps, medicines, foods, and perfumery.

No one knows how many seals of all kinds are killed every year. In the past a single steamer has brought back twenty-two thousand harp-seal skins. In the Newfoundland trade alone, in former days, more than half a million have been taken in a ten-day hunting season. One year three Russian ice-breakers in the White Sea got over thirty thousand each. On the other hand, if the cubs are scattered or weather is bad ships have come back with only two or three hundred. Laws now control the number of kills, and ships and men are lost in this dangerous trade, sometimes several ships in a year.

Nearly four thousand years ago the Chinese valued seal-furs highly. The Greek legend of the Golden Fleece is probably based on an ancient fur-trading expedition. For long periods in many lands, only those of royal blood were allowed to wear fur, and even to-day a nobleman's rank is shown by the amount of fur he wears on his ceremonial robes. To-day, too, the social rank of civilized women is generally indicated by their furs.

Fur has made the fortunes of many millionaire families— the Astors for example. In London, Leipzig, New York, Montreal, St Louis, Paris, Copenhagen, Seattle, and other cities great fur auctions are attended each year by people from every country. There are few women whose hearts have never been stirred by the sight of furs. And the world's supplies are swiftly dwindling; as the whale has been exterminated already from most areas of the oceans, and as the sea-cow has been wiped out, so all fur-bearing animals are being enormously reduced, the harp seals among them. Certain Eskimos and others who have no other means whereby to live are also threatened.

The sealers from the ship which had burst its way into the ice, north of Newfoundland, were rough seamen—ignorant and careless of all such problems. Their job was to slaughter seal-babies as fast as possible, and they went about it under the blackening sky with a will.

Suddenly from the distant ship there began the dismal and persistent wailing of a siren ordering their recall. The captain, biting his lips and shifting from one foot to the other, had watched the sky and left them at their flaying as long as he dared. Now the rising of the wind, the waking movements of the ice, and that fearful sky blackened with smoke forced him to call his killers off. With the siren bawling he waited feverishly for them to get back so that he could move his ship from this most perilous place.

The men straightened up; they tested the long ropes heavy with bleeding pelts; stuck knives back in sheaths; and turned wearily towards the vessel. As they did so, the wind uttered a shriek and everything was blotted out in such a barrage of bullet-like sleet that it seemed to be snowing upward.

The men, a moment ago bloody lords of all they saw, seemed to diminish to pygmies. The blasts of the siren were puffed contemptuously away. The sealers tumbling and clawing against the gale could not see the ship or each other. Worse, they could no longer see the snow-skinned waterways between the ice. There were sodden splashes and yells. The men's tiny voices, no louder than the seal-babies' cries had been, were whirled off into the snow-swirling void.

The captain, trying to be loyal to those who paid him, had sounded his recall signal half an hour too late.

20. The Ice Jaws shut

WHEN the ship had advanced on the seal-nursery the seals had seemed impotent. In a few hours thousands of their flayed hides had been tossed into its iron belly. Acres of ice were discoloured by red and steaming messes brutally jerked out of their skins.

But small and helpless as the seals had looked while submitting to the ship, their weakness was nothing compared with its powerlessness now.

Smothered by the billowing curtain of snow, one of the men hauling a heavy weight of hides stepped into an unseen water lead. The rope tangled round him, he could not see his mate, he could not even see the ice-edge from which he had fallen or anything but the down-pressing snow. Bawling for help, he heard a splash beside him. His mate had stumbled into the freezing water after him. Like so many seamen, this man could not swim. He clutched the other round the neck . . .

Blinded and stumbling, the other hunters on the ice finally found the ship. But when a hasty roll-call was shouted two were missing. Men peered uselessly into the white whirl, and the siren yelled over their heads as if the ship itself were shrieking to be taken away from the ice closing in on it. The captain waited and waited. He guessed they were dead, but he would not risk abandoning them alive in that white hell.

When at last his gloved hand moved the telegraph to full speed he felt already that his ship was doomed. He was an elderly man, he had commanded many ships, but never did one fight as gallantly as this one did, and his heart almost broke with a bitter pride.

Smash! she went into a floe that was moving up the water-lead to shut her in. The floe split, but another behind it majestically pressed the sharp crevasses shut and jammed the floe forward after the ship as she drew back to strike again.

Smoke pouring from her single funnel, she ground her whole weight furiously down on the white edge. It flinched, cracked away with a thunderous sound, and she drove hard into the damage. Men, whitened by snow as they clung along the rails, burst into cheering. They thought she was breaking free. But the captain, his lips snarling from pipe-yellowed teeth, knew better.

Yet while his ship could stir he meant to fight it out. He was one of those men who while they can move are never beat, a man who had always exulted in trying his strength against all the strength of the sea.

Crash! Once more he flung his ship at the ice. Again it went splitting and shattering away. One more blow like that and even now free water might be reached.

Then out of the white swirl two new ice-giants closed in on the ship. There remained now only one thing more to try. It was not a chance, for no real chance was left, but a duty in case some shift of the wind might miraculously give the ship back one hope of life. The captain's hand moved again on the telegraph. Even through the chaos of the storm every man heard the engine-room bell ring its changes, and they looked at their skipper with savage affection in their eyes.

The ship gathered way, sheared through some light ice, and then hit the tip of a great promontory in whose lee, if a way might be forced, some protection could be gained. She struck as if she had rammed the concrete side of a dock. A mast broke like a twig and thundered down over the deck. From below came a heart-rending cracking of wood and jarring of steel plates, while almost every man aboard lost his footing and went sprawling.

The ice-tongue, though it cracked, held. At once, a raft of ice from behind came smashing over the top of another floe and shut against the steamer's battered stern.

The captain's voice rose like a fog-horn above the din, ordering men on to the ice with towlines. Little black figures tumbled over the side, and towlines which had been held in readiness slithered after them in their gloved hands.

As they scrambled into position the ship's bell, set in motion by the movement of the wind and ice, solemnly began to toll—*BOOM-M-M . . . BOOM-M-M . . . BOOM-M-M. . . .* The captain's face turned towards the ill-omened sound, and he yelled an angry order. A man went doubling and running to the bell, struggled while it mouthed half-muffled protests, then gagged it with a jersey. The teams toiled at the towlines, the engines thudded till the vessel shook, and her bow hit the closing ice like an axe.

As she did so a mass of ice upreared over the gunwale, forced from beneath, and a lump weighing half a ton broke off and crashed down on the deck. Then a floe came rafting and sliding over another and hit the side of the steel ship, as the point of a walking-stick might hit a trapped rat.

This vessel, like most sealers, had been built to withstand the hammering of big tonnages of ice. But when ice rafts against a ship in a really bad storm the strongest works of man crumple like toys. Three ships were lost here in four days only a year or two ago. A few years back twenty-one vessels were crushed in the White Sea. Every sealer accepts the risk when he goes north for the springtime kill.

The ship was held still. She could move no more, and the ice-masses came crowding in with the gale behind them, like a mob for the kill.

The captain gave a shouted order to abandon ship. The vessel, kicked and shoved by irresistible pressures, was involuntarily climbing the ice she had failed to break. The snow was thinning, though the wind still cut like a knife. Overhead, through gaps in the feathery drift, came glimpses of dreadfully discoloured clouds.

The towlines lay abandoned, like dead snakes. The men still aboard hurled things down to others on the ice— clothes, cooking-pots, tinned goods, blankets, barrels of lard, sacks of potatoes, flour barrels, huge tarpaulins with which to make tents, sea-chests, even quantities of reeking hides that only an hour ago had covered the playful bodies of whitecoat babies.

To anyone not familiar with ice the seamen's unhurried air would have looked foolhardy. The rafting floes were piling against the ship's stern and climbing over the decks. Shock after shock jarred her to her centre. She climbed slowly, with convulsive efforts, up the ice ahead and tilted so that it became impossible to keep a footing on her decks. Most of the men were now on the ice. Except for occasional flurries, the snow had almost ceased. But daylight was beginning to fail and blacker darkness to fall.

Finally the captain came, slipping and sliding down the deck, clutching to his blue-coated figure a box containing the log and the ship's papers. He could have handed them down—he would have been safer with two hands to hold himself on the slanting deck—but he would rather have broken his neck than let those papers out of his grasp. The men were proud of him and made no offer of help.

He got down at last, losing his balance for the last few yards and rolling off the now almost vertical deck to land on his feet in the snow. Calmly and with dignity he stared around under his thatch of brow, and chose a site against the lee of a hummock for the tarpaulins to be erected. Then he gave orders for Primuses to be lighted, boiling cocoa to be made, and a radio-transmitter to be got to work crackling messages of their position.

It was useless for the Arctic to overwhelm this man. But he could be wounded yet. With a frightful shrill sound a raft of ice slowly ripped open his ship's steel side. The men on the floe stopped, in suspended attitudes, to watch.

With a deliberation that was scarcely bearable, the ice forced the vessel open to the guts. For a moment it was possible to see into the engine-room. Then there was a frightful explosion, and great gouts of scalding steam rushed up from the fires, dissolving the ice-tip into milky vapour. The stern of the ship sank visibly under its weight of ice, the bow rose, and the remaining mast snapped off against a hummock. Listing heavily to port, the vessel began to slide backward, the water came gushing in, and vast bubbles of air burst up. Savagely thrust down by the ice, she glided slowly below the waves. From the depths there rose a gush of air like a giant sigh, followed up by hundreds of whitecoat pelts swirling and swimming.

Only then did the captain turn away. At once the men began to shout and jostle, none of them looking at him. He stood for a moment with his back to the chaos where his ship had gone down, and gripped under one arm the papers that now were all that were left of her. Then he began to stump across the ice to the growing encampment.

There was plenty to be done. He had to have the shelters storm-rigged, ration out the provisions, see that every one had a big meal of steaming-hot food, doctor the skinner's bitten leg and another man's arm broken under the falling mast. Then he must see that radio-messages continued to be sent out, fire flares sent up into the night to attract other sealing-ships, and make the last bitter entries in his log.

But he was not thinking of any of that. He was seeing the thin, querulous face of the wife of one of the two lost seamen —she had come to the dockside to wave good-bye. It was the first time he had ever lost a man in the ice. He fumbled in his mind for words in which to tell her, to explain away something he had not seen and knew nothing about.

He turned with a growl on some men who were roping up a tarpaulin more like a lot of kids than sailors. A minute later, with a great hiss and a glow of light that painted all their upturned faces sickly green, the first flare went rushing up into the night sky.

A few miles away the seals were diving among the plunging floes, or suckling the few whitecoats that had been old enough to swim away from the butchers' acres the sealers had cleared.

Hundreds of nursing mothers had been bereft of their babies. They were fretful and swollen with milk, and licked their hot teats and shuffled about.

But the Wanderer shot arrow-like through the foam where ice-pans clashed. She danced between their deadly dancing, and dived shallow and swift as the mightier partners bowed so close that an underwater claw of ice almost shaved her back. Still too young to give the fruit of her body, the death of whitecoat cubs was no more to her than the melting of yesterday's snow.

L

21. Devil-fish

THE group of seals that had escaped the hunters' attack remained in the new place only for a few hours while stragglers rejoined them. Then they set off along the ice-edge, impelled to put more distance between themselves and any pursuing peril.

The Wanderer watched the ragged cubs who were shedding their baby coats and emerging in new grey fur. Many of them were still uncertain about swimming. They would tumble into the water, hold their heads too high, and go under backward. Almost at once they would reappear, snorting and gasping, paddling much too fast.

When they were a day or two older and had found that this plashing element could support them as well as any ice-floe they would fight small bits of floating ice, seize them, shake them, then release them, and dive at least a foot after an imaginary fugitive.

While the whitecoats were small it had not been uncommon for family groups to be seen, father, mother, and baby. But now all the adult males began to congregate on floes

distant from the females and cubs, swimming in packs together. Presently they began to disappear, groups going off
along the ice-edge and not returning. More and more of
the mature males followed till presently only mothers, cubs,
and adolescents remained, and even these tended now to
divide into separate groups.

The Wanderer began to notice a faint hostility towards
herself from the two-year-olds with whom she swam. Frightened by it, because she had been driven away from other
seal-herds, she nervously kept to the far edges of their
company. Once more the fur was starting to peel away
from her head. A timid unsociableness crept over her, and
a lethargy that could not be dispelled.

She turned wearily one day to find a quiet floe on which
to stretch herself. None of the patches of ice with which she
was familiar seemed safe. The very fact that she had visited
them with her companions made them unsuitable as a retreat
where others could not alarm her. She swam on and on
sluggishly under a kind of compulsion.

Far ahead she saw an area of ice blackened by seals lying
there in thousands. She felt an uneasy wish to hide among
these passive multitudes. She approached them warily.
Heads lifted here and there, but none seemed to resent her.
Diving, she swam under water to the edge of the ice and
surfaced, looking for a place to climb up. Most of the seals
seemed to be asleep. A few scratched, moved in a drugged
way, opened glazed and listless eyes. There was no enmity
against or even interest in her. She crept quietly between
them, though they lay so close that this was difficult.

All were moulting. With some of them, the mature males,
the process was nearly complete, only a few small patches of
dirty brown fur sticking to an almost perfect new coat.
With the adult females, moulting was about half-way. They
had new fur on heads, around fore-flippers, and on backs,
but a good deal of brownish old coat elsewhere. And there
were one or two adolescents of her own age with only the

first signs of moulting around the head and along the middle of the back.

She sank down thankfully beside these. After an hour or two she ceased to wake and look sharply around for signs of enmity. They still took no notice of her. She grew gradually comatose. The fur peeled stealthily off her head day by day as she grew dryer, taking with it a thin, dark, horny crust of skin. Later the moult spread about her body, the old hair being pushed off by a thick new coat of dark ashy grey. The youthful spots, which had been so distinctive, decreased in intensity. She was approaching five feet long now, and the strength and quickness normal to young wild things had been speeded in her case by her travels.

The Wanderer was growing up. With her slender hound-like head, large brown eyes, and strong young shapely body, she was becoming a beauty.

As soon as their new coats were fully exposed the males plunged cheerfully out of the moulting-lair. The adult females soon followed them. Presently only one or two un-seasonable old males, a handful of females, and a large number of adolescents were left.

The day came when the Wanderer also darted along the water and plunged towards her old playmates in their new coats.

Unmistakably they swam away from her. She was different from them. There was a clear contrast in her slightly larger size; and the markings of her coat were at variance with theirs. Having hunted and sported with her for months, they suddenly found her alarming. She swam timidly after them, a rapid defensive process at work in her. She had been refused with hostility earlier in her experience, and among wild things hostility always demands respect. Ignored, it may cost a life; those who face it must learn quickly from it.

Her hesitation sharpened their mistrust into fear, and fear, as always, grew into anger. When younger she had clung to the vicinity of her persecutors with the trust and weakness

of a dependent thing. Now, approaching adulthood, she
was more shy and more proud. Stinging with renewed vigour
after her moult, she circled as rapidly away from them as
they did from her. She swam out into deeper water and did
not return for two days. After that absence she appeared
to them more foreign than ever, and they turned at her with
angry snaps. Her nerve or patience broke. She swam away
again, this time in earnest.

Half an hour later all sounds of them had been forgotten.
She was alone, steadily and strongly swimming south, but
in a state of bewilderment. Instinct was moving in her blood,
trying to bring her back to her own tribe, by whom she
would be accepted. She had no memory of them, but her
body gave itself to the sea, as if seeking them. Unhappily
she was swimming in the opposite direction from them, so
far away in the North European ocean.

The springtime migration urge drove her on and on. For
many days she was nervous at being alone, and constantly
searched for company. But already she was too far south to
meet any of the western harp seals, who by this time were
gathering along the receding ice-edge for their journey into
far northern waters. She investigated many mysterious objects as she went, fled like a shadow at the approach of some,
chased others, and fed sparingly on crustaceans and varied
fish.

After some time her sense of loneliness faded. She had
crossed great stretches of ocean unaccompanied before. The
habits of those other journeys came back to reassure and
safeguard her. But the familiar contours of the ice-edge had
been left behind, and she grew increasingly ill at ease in
these strange sea-plains, without any instinct about how to
put this right.

She moved steadily south, past the Gulf of St Lawrence,
coming presently to a coast dotted with islands, immensely
indented and tasselated, with great tides swelling under her.
Had she been travelling with her old boon companions, they

would have ridden the white foam-horses into every bay, and played where the surf thundered round the feet of a hundred perilous cliffs. But the rising temperature of the southern air, so strange to an Arctic seal, hounded her on faster and faster, never staying to look aside, not even pausing for the fun of hunting fish, but swiftly and savagely taking only those which came in her path.

Once that headlong flight to the south was abruptly checked. Gliding along the coast, she came suddenly into waters populous with ships in the Boston steamer-track outside Massachusetts Bay. This reminder of the swimming monster that had dispersed the seals from their nursery sent the Wanderer diving down, and added the hateful speed of alarm to her swiftness. Surfacing only when it was necessary to breathe, she skirted Cape Cod and came almost at once to a halt.

It was as if she had swum through some invisible barrier into another world. Nowhere else on earth is there such a dramatic dividing line between two kinds of ocean life as here off Cape Cod. The very water itself, streaming up from the Gulf of Mexico area, seemed to her no longer cold, but almost steamy. It was full of unfamiliar shapes, and she shot to the surface to escape them.

Towards her shoulder along the top of the sea drifted a fleet of Portuguese man-of-war jelly-fish. Their gas-filled sails, about three inches high, were of translucent, shining pinky-blue, and their bright blue fishing-lines trailed like drift-nets several feet below the surface to windward. One of them held clasped in a bunch of these tentacles tight against its many mouths a large dead fish.

The attitude of the fish sent the Wanderer gliding deep again for safety, and this perhaps saved her life. A single touch from the poisoned fishing-lines of one of these semi-tropical creatures can have serious results even to a man, while anyone who gets really entangled is lucky to avoid death. Yet the Wanderer as she dived saw a dozen fishes, like minnows, playing in immunity among the tentacles of each man-of-war. These little pensioners, living on crumbs from their masters' tables, and going everywhere with them, are protected not only from their death-rays but also from all who might otherwise feed on them. It is said that a thick slime coating keeps them immune from the stinging rays. Probably the minnows serve the men-of-war somehow in return, for evolution wastes very little. These men-of-war in the world's northern hemisphere have even developed their sails at an angle the reverse of that of their own kind in the southern hemisphere, in each case to adapt them better for food-hunting and safety in the winds and currents of their own seas.

Leaving this perilous fairy fleet far behind, and plunging on instead of back, because she could not relate action to apprehension, the Wanderer found herself among strange fishes of colours and shapes alarming to her. The unpleasant warmth of the water filled her with physical distress. She travelled miserably on, keeping under the water part of the time, but equally ill at ease whether on the surface or down in the hot depths.

After some time of journeying the sea grew cooler again, though not nearly so cold and refreshing as her beloved Arctic Ocean. She had got into the "Cold Wall" of water which keeps the Gulf Stream away from most of the United States coasts, and which, if it could be diverted and replaced by its warmer neighbour, might make New York almost like Florida. Despite this cooler water, she sensed a greater strangeness about her day by day. Sometimes she tried to approach the shore. But there were appearances there that roused instincts of escape in her—stains of smoke in the sky, distant ships, shapes and sounds to which even she was too timid to draw near.

One morning when rain flung a haze over the sea the Wanderer went diving for fish to satisfy her nervous, nagging hunger. She had been travelling hard, and she was lean and uneasy.

Deep below her she saw a rocky sea-bottom with sand
drifted between honeycombed stones. A group of small
shrimps went swimming hastily by, and she darted down to
investigate. There was a place where two rocks had been
thrown together by the tide and half silted up with sand.
Between them was a knife-like cleft, and outside this lay a
heap of crab-shells, some of them very big. There were no
crabs in them; they had been sucked out clean as if they had
never been there. The Wanderer floated down to examine
these shells as she would curiously examine anything that
was novel and did not frighten her.

The shells lay there; some partly filled with sand. They
offered no clue to the riddle of their emptiness. The Wanderer's eyes glanced sharply about, instinctively watching
on every side for danger or for some tit-bit of food.

As she slid past the rocks a long dark arm, like an ele-
phant's trunk, shot from the cleft and curled tightly about
her body. At the first touch of that loathly cold encirclement,
and before she could make a stroke to free herself, two other
arms whipped after the first, trying to grip her round and
drag her between the rocks.

For a frightful flash of time she saw in the crevice the
prominent cold eyes of a devil-fish bulging towards her, and
a black horny beak strong enough to pierce the thickest
lobster-shell protruded from the centre of a new bunch of
trunks that were shooting out at her.

22. *The Friendly Creature*

THE devil-fish was not merely using that cleft of rock for a hunting-base. She had transformed it into a fantastic sea-nursery.

Originally she must have felt that the slit between the rocks was too big, though it was, in fact, so narrow that it seemed impossible so large and powerful a creature could have drawn herself into it. But she had fortified it further by dragging and wedging into the bottom of the slit several very large crab-shells, which greatly decreased its size. In the remaining opening she hung brooding, her dreadful eyes unsleepingly on the watch for anything that should approach to menace her private maternity home.

Behind her she had hung up on the rock about fifty thousand eggs in long bunches, like clusters of grapes. When not hunting or warning off intruders she would pass one arm under the hanging bunches of eggs, dilate the membrane on each side of the limb into a sort of giant spoon, and then lift, turn, and caress them. Then she would carefully cleanse them with water drawn into her body and jetted out again, to prevent any undersea parasites from taking a grip on them.

These eggs were near to hatching after several weeks of unremitting, faithful care, and it was to that fact that the Wanderer owed her life. A brooding octopus loses flesh and grows weaker, as a hen does while incubating her eggs. The octopus, so terrible to other inhabitants of the deep, is very often such an unselfish mother that she dies of exhaustion immediately her eggs hatch. This devil-fish was weak and half starved, because she had refused to move out and leave her eggs unguarded, even when the creatures she needed for her daily food no longer swam near her lair.

At the sight of the Wanderer blundering past, the devil-fish's mud colour had changed to a furious dark red. By instinct she flung out several of her eight arms, each equipped with two rows of suckers. Because of her enfeebled condition, and because they failed to find a firm surface in fur, the suckers did not get an instant grip, and with a convulsive leap the Wanderer slithered sideways and away. Her heart was pounding, her head turned as she doubled to and fro to discover how best to dodge pursuit. But there was no pursuit. The octopus withdrew her trunk-like arms inside the crack of the rock. Slowly she changed colour as her fury abated, back from muddy red to muddy green. She seemed to shrink. After watching vainly for some other food to float near, she turned back to her bunches of eggs and began wearily and instinctively to fondle and turn them. The eggs were due to hatch, but the mother had not many hours to live.

The Wanderer swam on down the coast. For a few minutes she was in a state of terror. Never again would she go near undersea heaps of crab-shells or narrow clefts in sea-bottom rocks, because a new impulse of avoidance had been added to the reactions of her brain.

Her dangerous curiosity was undiminished. Half an hour after it had carried her almost literally into the mouth of death she was peering with every nerve alert at a new stimulant. Gliding idly along just above the sea-bottom not far out from the coast, she had come upon a dim battlefield

of pygmies, the assault of a Lilliputian army upon a sub-marine Siegfried Line. A huge assembly of sea-stars was attacking an oyster-bed.

Fifty thousand bushels of these sea-stars are sometimes removed in a year from oyster-beds off the Connecticut coast, and this is only one part of the invading forces that creep stealthily about the sea-bottom there. The Wanderer floated a foot or two overhead, watching the final storming of one undersea castle. It was a big oyster, several inches across, who had escaped the daily perils of existence for ten or twelve years.

Born in a puff of spawn with about ten million 'twins,' he was now the sole survivor. Crablets, prawns, jelly-fish, starfish, basket-snails, whelks, tingles, sponges, worms, bar-nacles, conches, innumerable disease germs, all had taken their toll. Human animals had eaten a good number of this oyster family. Storm turbulence had suffocated hundreds with overlayers of sand.

Many of these enemies had vainly attacked this old sur-vivor. Once a tingle had bored a hole with his rasping tongue clean through the thickness of the veteran's shell. Then some passing sea-hunter licked the tingle off and ate him, and the oyster repaired the hole with new shell from inside.

But now, to-day, while the Wanderer watched, the end came for this last of ten million brothers. A five-armed sea-star, marching at the rate of six inches a minute with a great regiment of its kind through the jungles and over the Saharas of the sea-bottom, leapt upon the veteran's armoured back. Fixing the suckers of two arms on one valve of the oyster-shell and three arms on the other, it strained to straighten its rays. An oyster can withstand a sudden pull, but must eventually surrender before a sustained one.

The Wanderer, floating motionless overhead, stared down through the wavering water and saw the gates of the oyster's castle slowly forced open. The sea-star, never for a second relaxing its tremendous pull, extruded its stomach through its mouth and began to digest the helpless inhabitant of the shell. Like man, it ate the oyster alive.

All around, the army of attackers were disembowelling other oysters, or hurrying across the submarine landscape to seize free ones. One sea-star can eat half a hundred victims, each almost its own size, in a week. Attaining rapid maturity, these pygmies can reproduce thousands of their own kind from each adult.

A tremor through the water announced a newcomer, and the Wanderer glided away. The new thing—clumsy, but of overwhelming size—swam slowly along the surface of the sea while the seal made a circle to watch it. It was a dredger, heralded by a boiling cloud of disturbed sand and mud.

The vessel's scoop spooned up a hundred pounds of oysters, rocks, crabs, starfish, and other indiscriminate things. The men on the ship swore at what they found—empty shells, shells in the last stages of attack, and countless glutted sea-stars. Oyster-beds are not left unpoliced by men for long, but enemies swimming and marching to attack them never rest night or day. With methodical movements the two-legged allies of the little victims set to work to pick out and destroy the sea-stars, fling back the oysters, and so turn the tide of that undersea battle. But by that time the Wanderer had gone two miles on her southward way.

The sea-surface activities of human creatures outside the Hudson river estuary sent her curving far out from the coast. Having sunk over the western horizon everything that alarmed her, she found leisure to feel again the discomfort of isolation.

As she swam she saw a creature advancing over the sea towards her. It towered more formidable than any iceberg, it glided towards her swifter than any shark. When she slid away to one side it seemed not to see or pay any attention to her, but glided majestically forward on its chosen way. Dark below, white in its upper parts, and with two slits,

like eyes, in front, it was accompanied by a drifting plume of
smoke, and far around it the seas shivered from the beat of
its going.

The Wanderer was not alarmed now that the liner failed
to pursue her. She was interested. She swam a little nearer.
As it drew level with her point of watch there spewed from
its side a rain of something that in another creature might
have been spawn—hundreds of bread-rolls flung overboard
by the stewards after luncheon had been cleared away.

In any creature of the seas the sight of another spawning
stimulates a deadly interest. Fishes darted in clouds to the
foam-spread path the liner had left. They went to try whether
this softening white roe could be eaten, and behind them
came their natural hunters, the Wanderer among them.

To the finny scavengers, gracefully turning in the water
around the sinking crumbs, the darkness of the seal passing
overhead was a deadly threat. She went gliding among them,
looking them over with her liquid brown eyes. Reaching
over, she took one in her teeth.

The fish leapt in her jaws. She was not hungry, having
fed only half an hour before. But, feeling this struggle against
her mouth, she sat upright in the water, holding the captive
in her forepaws while she nibbled the soft of its belly. It
jerked convulsively twice with more force than seemed possible in so small a thing, and then hung with open mouth
panting out its life.

She did not see the two dorsal fins sticking up like triangular sails, one fifty feet behind the other, cutting through the
sea towards her. At the last minute she must have heard
something—she vanished as if plucked from beneath. The
leading killer-whale foamed over the spot like a twenty-foot
plough, his two-inch-wide teeth snapping shut with a sound
like a trap.

The snap missed the Wanderer's back so narrowly that
the fish she had held struck the white eye-patch on the
whale's black head. His mate dived under him, and failed

by a hairbreadth to grip the seal as she flew down into the depths.

She rushed along, doubling like a hare, and the killers came flying after her. Neither had eaten for some time, and that had impaired their strength a little. They felt in all their nerves the sensation of the crunch across her back and the taste of blood that these hunting efforts almost always preceded. They combined to head her off, each turning the seal into the path of the other. She fled with bounding heart, with sight that grew strained, bloodshot, and dim.

As she dived away from a vast wallow above her neck, the sea-floor in front abruptly shelved upward, a sloping wall in her path.

She never knew that the whales were forced to turn in one colossal swirl because they were too big to follow her up the beach, or that they raced away, forgetting what they had pursued, hunting for anything that might meet their savage eyes.

She struggled on, her heart almost bursting. A wave lifted her and flung her forward. As the water sucked away beneath her, growling over the pebbles, she flapped up the beach with two or three convulsive movements to a place out of reach of the throw of the waves.

A startled human voice cried out. Dripping like a big dog, looking up with eyes hardly able to focus for weakness and terror, she saw a pinkish-yellow upright blur in front of her. From it she sensed, as all animals can, the atmosphere of love.

She did not associate this yellow-haired girl in a yellow swim-suit with the Eskimo hunters or the sealers, who were the only other creatures of this kind she had seen. This one was friendly. The Wanderer was terrified by pursuit, and had to find shelter from death. So she did a thing seals have sometimes done before.

With a final flop she flung herself at the feet of the friendly creature. There she lay with closed eyes, quivering, too exhausted to stir again, waiting for whatever might happen.

The girl, afraid to move lest the seal vanish, gave a cooing sound that had in it both maternal and childish rapture, then called in a low, urgent voice to her friend along the beach.

23. *Sea-floor Saraband*

THE Wanderer's eyes opened and rested on the human
animal who stood over her, resisting a temptation to
touch. The man who had been called walked quickly along
the beach to her side. He was big, muscular, sun-tanned,
wearing an old faded pair of bathing-trunks. From him too
the Wanderer felt the emanation of friendly fearlessness.

They talked in swift, excited voices above her head, while
with long breaths she regained strength and lost some of the
fear of pursuit. She grew aware again of the sound of breakers hissing up the beach behind her, calling her back to her
natural element. Overhead white clouds sailed in a sunny
sky.

She sneezed violently, and tears flowed from her eyes, at
which the two creatures burst into an alarming explosion of
laughter.

Startled by the sound, the Wanderer flung round, hunched
herself, and started down the beach at an undulatory gallop.
A wave bigger than the rest came riding up the beach, and
the Wanderer slipped into it like a bird into a bush.

As if giving a swimming display for the two on the beach,

she slid over the contours of the incoming waves, streaked round a curl of surf, turned on her back and rolled over, corkscrewed up out of the water like a jumping salmon, swayed, dived out of sight. The two friendly creatures were standing holding hands, and their laughter bounded across the empty surface of the sea.

The Wanderer did not know it, but chance had changed her destiny. Flying from the killers, she had been driven north, back on her tracks in the direction from which she had been travelling for so long. Still afraid of the arc of ocean from which they had chased her, she kept on towards her own cold world again.

She was in poor condition. For weeks she had travelled hard. Her solitary alertness, vital because she could not share a herd's communal watchfulness, wore her down. The fish and crustaceans she ate, though of the same kinds that she had relished in Polar waters, did not feed her body so well, because they were less oily and fat.

Yet now she was instinctively soothed because she was heading towards the home of her race instead of away from it. She glided rapidly along by day and night. Sometimes she seemed to be the only thing in an enormous circumference of blue and swaying water. Sometimes she passed seething mobs of creatures, a few huge, some her own size, but mostly small enough to be plunged among when she was interested in their doings.

Not all these inhabitants of the deeps were alive. One night she glided slowly past a submerged submarine, a two-thousand ton steel shape slinking on some secret mission, almost as far from home as the Wanderer herself. Once or twice she saw steamers, and swam out of reach of them, trying not to attract their attention. Some defence mechanism in her now associated steamers with danger, because in the past ships had brought creatures to chase her. Ships now seemed to her something to avoid.

One windy night she overcame her reluctance to approach

M

these metallic swimmers of the seas. Coming up from a dive, she saw ahead of her a strange thing.

A wavering black line trailed through the water, visible from where the Wanderer swam by the penetration of moon-light through the sea. At intervals on spur-traces along this line a variety of hooked fishes leapt and jerked. Most of them were cod, and the Wanderer, though she was full-fed, never could resist the desire to swim after cod.

She glided up towards one, and was startled that it did not rush away. Instead, it thumped up and down with its nose to the line. She bit it and saw it flop down and hang quivering on the hook. Then she began to move up the line and bite a fish here and there in a fascinated sort of way. She had never known cod wait like this until they were bitten. They vibrated and jumped, but made no attempt to escape.

Working along the trawler's line, she did enormous damage to the hundreds of hooked fish. The line was anchored and buoyed up at intervals, and as she came up near one of these buoys to breathe she saw a ship quite near her. The trawler tossed in Indian-ink black against the sky while the fishermen examined another line.

As the Wanderer surfaced, her head breaking the water made a splotch of silver on the side of a big wave and a sailor noticed her. He spoke in low tones to another fisherman, and together they leaned on the trawler's rail and watched the seal. They knew what she was about; they would have shot her, but they had no gun aboard. As the ship rose and fell the two swore fatalistically, and others gathered round them. The Wanderer dived again. She went slowly about in the dimness biting pieces out of fishes' sides and letting the pieces fall from her jaws. Presently the lines were all drawn in, and she swam away.

Then she surfaced again and sniffed with delight. A storm was rising, and the wind seemed to force through and through her body while the fierce lift of the waves challenged her to play. The Wanderer slid swiftly up to the wavetops and flew racing down, she sat upright in the spume while it spun her body round and smacked her with a burst of shimmering spray.

Almost at once she saw the steam-trawler again, wildly tossed, and as she went she heard a shout and saw a splash. A man had been washed overboard by a climbing wave. She dived for safety and found, ten feet under, the drowning man hurrying along backward in a grotesque caricature of walking. His head lolled sideways, then rolled down on his chest, his arms flew slowly wide and gestured, his legs took forty-foot strides as he passed her by. Now he seemed to run abruptly uphill until his head almost broke the surface, now contentedly marched down and down and down.

She followed him at a discreet distance, ready to turn and dive away, but watching the slow and extravagant curving of his limbs. He turned round, as though walking backward bored him, and started to glide forward at a great pace on his knees. Then he stood suddenly upright, spun like a teetotum, and began again that macabre *pas de seul* as he bowed and mowed and sidled away from his mermaid follower.

A week or two later, still going north, she came upon a wrecked ship. From far away she saw a cloud of disturbance on the sea-floor. Fish darted to and fro, and mud clouds slowly drifted up as the sea stirred the vessel a little, displacing the ooze in which it lay. From all this, its great rusty funnel stuck up forlornly. As she watched, something flashed between her and it.

She drifted towards the wreck, ready to vanish if anything emerged. The ship had been there a long time, and had sunk down in the slime. Succulent streamers of weed waved a nightmare invitation. Sand and mud had silted up over one side of the hull, and some sort of worm life writhed and gorged under this drifted bank, faintly stirring it and extruding hundreds of stiff mud tubes from it. Barnacles clung to the steel plates, crusting them like stony warts. In and out of the broken hatches fishes played and hunted or drifted round with fixed and startled eyes.

The Wanderer circled the wreck twenty times, surfaced above it, dived down to it again. She examined it from every angle, and because she was the biggest creature there everything else moved away from her.

This ship, a cargo-steamer, had been footing it north on a grey afternoon after a three-day gale had left the ocean tumbling under a ragged sky. Wallowing through the water hills, she had suddenly struck something awash—an ice-floe melted down like a raft and swept with a creeping acre of foam. It had ripped the front out of the ship, and she had settled by the head, plunging under in five minutes.

The Wanderer swam again and again close to the ragged rent in the sunk vessel's bow. Fishes darted in there to escape this floating shadow, and presently they came speeding out, only to turn and race back again at sight of her still there. She had no motive for exploring that appallingly risky gash with the muddy sea stirring in and out of it, but presently she went in, straining her eyes through the darkness. She got into the interior of the hull and found a man there. Most of the crew had got away, many diving off as the vessel plunged, swimming to boats and rafts. But this man had been killed when the bows caved in, and his body was trapped where a broken girder pinned him.

There was not much left of him. As the Wanderer drifted past, such a mob of crabs scuttled sideways from the place that she spun about and raced out to the sea again. Nothing pursued, and an hour afterwards she re-entered the broken bows, eventually emerging through one of the hatches.

That night she began to move on north. But before long the attraction of the sunken ship pulled her round. As she again neared the wreck she grew aware of a new thing there much bigger than herself. A steel monster of the same kind as the sunken one now stood guard on the surface.

She was presently reassured by the quietness of this ship
hove to in the darkness. At daybreak the salvage-ship began
making preparations to send down a diver to the wreck.

His bulky figure, no stranger than other shapes in the
deeps, slid down presently through the water and found the
sea-floor. Padded like a rag doll, with electric shoulder-
lights, glass-fronted and grated helmet, and with clamps for
hands, the diver walked slowly about in his lead-weighted
boots. The Wanderer lurked at a safe distance off, watching
him. Once when his lights pierced in her direction as he
turned she shivered a quarter of a mile away, though she
had been far beyond the diver's vision, and he certainly was
not thinking about catching seals.

As he made no attempt to follow her she came back and
floated comfortably far off, watching him. He moved dully,
awkwardly putting aside fronds of sea-tangle, surrounded by
fishes that sometimes glided to within a few inches of his
head. Attracted by the lights, they flashed in and out of the
beams like little silver darts.

The diver began systematically to search the sea-floor, and
soon found his way to the side of the wreck. He made several
slow endeavours to climb up the sand and ooze and get on
to the deck, but seemed hampered by his padded suit.
Presently he went floating away upward, and the Wanderer
followed him, still far off, and saw him drawn on to the
salvage-ship.

She loitered about for some time, and watched him make
two more descents. Once, having grown careless of his slow
movements, she drifted too close and was caught in the beam
of the electric lights as he turned. He peered sharply through
the glass of his helmet as he saw the big body of the seal
flash away out of his sight. Then he turned again to his work.

The Wanderer might have stayed watching that strange
sea-floor saraband for days, for she found something irresistibly attractive about the silver glints of the fishes in the
diver's lights, the coiling down of innumerable cables to the

wreck, the stabbing sparkle of an underwater acetylene burner, the scurrying of clouds of disturbed crabs, and especially the slow, waving movements of the diver's limbs.

But next morning, after much creaking and preparation aboard the salvage-ship, a new monster was lowered into the water. It was an electrically driven submarine tractor, like a tiny tank, riveted and dully shining, sliding down on cables to the swirl of the sea-floor.

The diver busied himself for some time with it. Then it began to crawl forward towards the sunken ship under its own power, giving out a sound terrible to all the secret watchers of the wreck. It was too much for the Wanderer. The thing frightened her, and she went shimmering away.

24. Battle of Leviathans

THE Wanderer's puppyish looseness and lack of co-
ordination were gone. She looked shapely, strong,
torpedo-swift. Her colour was becoming an almost uniform
grey, and the dark spots of youth had mostly faded.

There was an air about her, too, apart from her charac-
teristic colouration, which spoke clearly of approaching
young maturity. It was visible in the gentle and playful
angle of her head and present in the shy but inviting brown
eyes. She looked upon her world of heaving water with that
sunny royalty belonging everywhere to youth that stands at
last on the threshold of its kingdom.

As there were changes in her appearance, so the chemistry
of her body was becoming adult and sending through every
nerve and vein its strong demands. Now, at nearly two and a
half years old, race instincts, as powerful as the life-force
itself, were calling her home. For the first time she was finding not only disturbance, but also guidance from them.

As she swept north towards the tip of Greenland something
like a magnet of the heart kept edging her east. There was
nothing to recognize in the swelling hills of the sea, yet she

grew uneasy when a fish-hunt took her west, and felt comfort
whenever she veered towards Northern Europe again.

For a time she was in an unpleasant warm area of the sea.
Then the water became colder. The Labrador Current
sweeping south had met and joined with the Gulf Stream
going north, and here the two combined to send a drift east
in the direction of her distant home.

The Wanderer, joyously refreshed, hurried along with the
swing of the water. As she swam the sea grew rougher where
the two great ocean currents struggled for supremacy, and
one morning she saw ahead such whirlpools in the waves
that she sheered away. She moved on in a great arc around
the North Atlantic south of Greenland and Iceland in the
direction of the North British coast.

Then came an afternoon when a wispy sea fog melted,
and the whole surface of the ocean looked like a faintly
billowing satin quilt. It was empty under a blue and cloudless sky. A summery breeze, warm and salt-scented, whispered over the plash-plash of waves, and the Wanderer sat
bolt upright in the midst of it, head and shoulders out of the
water, sunning herself.

Far away she noticed the white flash of a bird sitting on
the water. When a wave lifted her she could see it—then as
she sank the bird was cut off from view. She looked for it
each time she rose. She was up on high now and there was
the bird in plain view . . . and as she watched it vanished.

The Wanderer fell down from her throne in the wavetop,
and found herself swimming towards the place. What had
happened was a contradiction of the natural laws to which
she was accustomed. The bird had not flown up. It had not
dived. It was sitting probably asleep on the top of the water
one moment—and not sitting there the next.

No seal could have looked on this impossibility without
going to investigate, and of all seals the Wanderer least of
any. She almost flew through the water in her anxiety to
reach the place where the bird had vanished. And so she

blundered into a battle of leviathans in which—luckily for her—she was noticed no more than a mouse might be running between the feet of fighting men.

The bird had been sucked down from underneath and eaten by one of a party of killer whales. Half a dozen of these killers, desperate from starvation, had combined to run down and destroy creatures that one alone could not kill. They had been scouring the ocean for days with no more reward than seabirds and fish, not enough to satisfy them, but only to whet their avidity.

The lucky one who had floated up under the seabird was dashed at by the rest so that for a moment it seemed as if there might be a cannibal fight. But in the same second one of them glimpsed far down below a quarry which would be enough to glut them all.

It was a finback whale, twice as big as the biggest twenty-five foot hunter. Dark backed, white bellied, with a mouth that looked big enough to cut a killer in two, actually she was defenceless. They knew by instinct that this mild leviathan, an eater of crustacea and small fishes, was almost powerless to fight against them. But the avidity with which the six creatures swam down in pursuit was intensified by something more than their instinctive sense of advantage over the giant. The whale was accompanied by a calf not as big as one of themselves, and no more dangerous than a lamb.

Alone the old finback mother by sheer strength and endurance might have shaken off this monstrous pack. Or had a running fight begun, she might have struck one with her tail, mortally injuring it, and its companions might have turned on it and torn it to bits while she got away. Hampered by a calf, her chances were grim.

The killers were led by an old male whose distorted flippers and triangular back-fin five feet high showed his age, as well as adding to the speed with which he could drive and turn his enormous body. With primordial ferocity this veteran plunged at the finback whale's mouth. Whales have immovable lips—this twenty-five ton headlong attack was launched with the usual deadly intent of seizing the victim's tongue.

A whale is warm-blooded, breathing the air by lungs, without scales on the skin, with hands of the five-fingered type, with a skeleton, heart, blood-vessels, and a brain at least as well developed as that of a horse or dog. It can feel pain and is conscious of fear. Its affection for its calf is striking.

This leviathan reacted to the attack on herself by turning away to guard her baby. She was barely in time. Four of the killers surrounded it, one was in the act of gripping its tail to stop it moving while a second tried to drag back its upper jaw and expose the tongue for the others to tear it out.

Their combination was as swift and sure as a football team, and less than a second more was needed. But the mother whale churned among them like a battleship among destroyers, and before that rush the quartette scattered, one of them missed by an inch by the thrash of her stupendous tail.

The old killer leader was hit in passing by the swell of her back with a force that almost broke the lower jaw from his mouth. He rolled away, his small eyes suffused with blood. But there was a sixth attacker, a female, the smallest of them, almost as small as the calf now wallowing along in terror under its mother's lee. This savage killer female had hung back on the outskirts of the tremendous turbulence, watching, and as the mother whale turned it went in like a terrier and grasped at the root of a smashing fluke. Its teeth chopped through the toughness of muscles and grated together.

The whale gave one spasmodic lurch of her body and the biter was flung twenty feet through the water. But its work was done. The only part of her body the mother whale could use in clumsy defence was now partly disabled.

Racing away at the top speed of which her calf was capable, she seemed for a moment to have broken up that united attack and scattered the killers. Two of them were hurt. Had the blow of her back been a little more direct, the old leader would have been crippled for long enough to let the victims escape, for the rest seemed unwilling to renew the attack without his savagery to guide them. But in the killer leader's brain there was rage enough to overcome his hurt. He slewed round and flung himself at twice their speed along the fugitives' bubbling trail. Behind him the other five closed in.

This time all six went for the calf together. There was a swirl of black and white bodies as one of the killers got the calf by the tail and held him while another bit into the side of his head. As the rest bumped each other in their hunger for a grip, the mother whale ploughed among them.

They dropped the calf and turned at her together. One of them, diving and missing a bite, was struck full in the head by her half-crippled tail. The attacker rolled over and over, sinking away out of sight. But the odds were too great. The leader gripped one of her lips and tearing at it began to swim with his entire force away from her. Unable to bite anything bigger than a fish the monster, like a sinking liner dragged by a sinking tug, slowly and involuntarily turned that way. Another killer bit deep into her throat.

Spurred by agony she arched her back and ripped clear of them both. But she was badly wounded, unable any longer to continue a battle in which she had no weapon but her weight against this pack of tigers of the sea. She flung round, blindly cannoning against them, bursting through them as they tried to seize her in several places. Bleeding, stiff, in dire need of air, she stumbled off through the green dimness leaving her calf to its fate.

The killers swirled about it, tore its jaws open, seized its tongue. In a minute its dead body was sinking while they tore at its head, gouging and dragging out lumps of flesh.

Like a mob of devils boiling round something hidden by their crowding, the whole scene sank slowly into the depths.

24. *The Grey People*

THE Wanderer stumbled into the area of this undersea battle in its brief lull while the whale and her calf were trying to escape after the smashing of the first united attack.

She did not get very near—one dim and awful glimpse of a killer shape sent her round on her tracks. Away she went, diving deeper and deeper. All sounds and signs of the fight were left behind in twenty strokes, but she pounded on and on. She had had enough of killers.

When her fear had faded she swam on in a timeless and happy manner, yet with a growing restlessness in her body that she could not ease. It dragged her round eastward, somewhere near the sea-bottom ridge that stretches under the waves from Iceland past the Faroe Islands and separates the Atlantic Ocean from the Norwegian Sea. As the sun rose and set, and the moon waxed to full and waned again to a silver sickle over the waves, she had many adventures.

Sometimes she got into the vicinity of danger, but she was no longer an impulsive cub. As inquisitive as ever, she was now more circumspect. Lessons learned by wild things leave impressions in the blood of those who can survive them.

She came one stormy night in early winter to a rock like a giant's tooth sticking out of phosphorescent breakers. She heard the thunder of waves on granite walls long before they could be seen, and presently she was aware of foam bursting up its sides and pouring down again while the storm-wrack fled overhead between cold and steely glitters of the moon.

She plunged and leapt forward with the rollers, going so near that it seemed that she must be hurled broken against that sullen rock-face. But always at the last second she slithered sideways and away, exquisitely using the force of the water to lift her clear.

This was Rockall, its sides too steep for her to climb, a castle-perilous, moated by the cold sea, guarded by birds who stood or marched to and fro on its sloping top, or took off and glided in grey patrols about it.

On a December morning of watery sunshine the Wanderer approached the island of the grey seals north-west of Scotland. There was an immense swell, and the sea was more white than green. The waves would have been higher still, but they were flattened by a wind that would have blown a man down. But there were no men on this sea-rounded, barnacle-studded mass of rock. Instead it was lichened with the dark iron-grey of innumerable seals lying as quietly as if dead.

The Wanderer, tossing in the foam, knew they were not dead, and her blood throbbed with excitement at being no longer alone. She saw that these were strange creatures, far bigger than her own kind, rounder of head, thicker of neck, lacking the harp seal's lovely streamlined shape.

She allowed the waves to drift her close, casually flipping herself away from a rock-point smothered in bursting spray, and watched the strangers, letting them see her head peering inquisitively from the boil of waters.

They were very silent. They lay still, not quarrelling, not taking any notice of each other. Occasionally one raised its head and uttered a mournful cry that had in it the sound of surf. The hair on some of them was very light-coloured, and in places a carpet of this hair was shed on the rocks. These seals were in the last stages of changing their coats, for grey seals have a moulting season different from their Arctic cousins.

Had this been summertime, when the seal-rocks resounded day and night with bleats and barks and little cries, she would never have dared to land. But now the strangers mostly took no notice of her, and the few who looked her way saw her with listless eyes. So she slid into a sheltered creek between the island and a rocky outcrop in the sea, and, seizing her moment when the water was quieter, slithered up out of its reach.

For an hour she lay there, resting and content. Though the nearest of the strangers was a hundred feet away, she felt happily part of a community once more. Yet this was different from her former attempts to attach herself to a tribe of strangers. Now she had no intention of mixing with them. She did not try to drag herself among them. She did not want to play or hunt with them, and when later that day half a dozen lolloped down to the sea, she remained where she was. It was simply that after months of solitary wandering she was soothed merely to be near seals again.

During the day the gale died, leaving the evening sky pale and clear, and the rollers sliding from horizon to horizon. Never had the Wanderer known such peace. The other seals took no more notice of her than if she had been a log washed up by the sea.

They slept. Some lay high up on the rocks, far above where the Wanderer could have climbed. Some were seaweed-coloured, some were spotted, some fairly light. They were grouped about anyhow, many side by side, others with heads together. Often they yawned, stretched themselves, wiped their noses with their flippers. Sometimes one would flounder sleepily to a more comfortable couch of rock.

Once, to the Wanderer's alarm, one of them growled and

snarled, lowed like wind blowing through a sea-cave, dived off into the water, puffing and blowing, surged against a sloping face of rock and tried to hold on with the strong nails of his flippers. He was washed away again, and slid lazily out to sea as one making the best of what had to be. Presently he returned, landed, and crawled back towards the place he had vacated. His flat rear stuck up vertically a little forward of his hind-flippers, as he lumped across the rocks. He moaned, raised his whiskery head irritably two or three times, then sank down and slept.

The Wanderer stayed there several days, but she avoided the others, and took no part in their lives. Once one of them loped over the rocks towards her, and she dived into the sea, not returning for two or three hours.

Some of them went fishing, and she kept respectfully clear of them. She saw one come up with a big fish which it crunched, then bolted whole with a backward toss of the head. A bit of fish was sheared off, and before the seal could turn and retrieve it a gull had dived, seized it without pausing in its glide, and gone sailing up and away. The seal leapt up at the bird with the grace of the gull itself, and re-entered the sea in a shining curve. A moment later it was sitting up in the same spot with another fish in its mouth, apparently looking round to be sure the coast was clear before disposing of this one.

The seas shimmered with finny food. The Wanderer was able to swim away by herself, find a passing pollack, saithe, or mackerel, and enjoy a solitary meal before returning to land on the same bit of rock as before.

One morning she came up from a dive and found a motor-boat drifting silently with its engine at rest. In the boat were three men, and one was playing on a mouth-organ an ancient island croon called *The Seagull from the Land-under-Waves*. They saw the seal's head break the water, and one spoke in a whisper to the musician telling him to keep on playing.

The speaker knew that music attracts seals. The

Wanderer was too cautious to go near the boat, though the sounds almost moved her flippers despite herself. She hesitated, half her length showing, every nerve alert for a dive, yet unable to plunge till something occurred to break the spell.

One of the men in the boat was a naturalist on his way out to make some observations of seals during moulting. He was excited at seeing an Arctic harp seal so far from home, though he knew they are occasionally recorded on the British coasts. With a slowness and caution learnt from many disappointments in fields and woods and on rocky islets he raised a camera. The musician, hardly aware, perhaps, of what was going on, because he loved so much this wistful croon a MacCrimmon piper had stolen from a fairy hill, passed his lips across his instrument and stared dreamily into the Wanderer's mermaid eyes.

Click! went the camera. She was six feet deep and still gliding down. The naturalist had taken an observation of her; she had also recorded one of him, a slow, two-legged animal with horn-rims around his eyes, his hair and rough tweed jacket in an advanced state of moult. Like a true scientist she felt no emotion; the habits of this intrusive specimen were extraneous to the fish behaviour she had come out that morning to study.

When she got back to her rocky island she found that a number of the inhabitants were gone. They had finished their moult and sped off to sea for a heavy feed after the starvation and little death from which they had emerged. Each day some of the grey seals flappered over the rocks, plunged into the sea, and capered away towards distant hunting-grounds.

But the Wanderer was content to stay. She lay interminably watching the tides rise and fall as the ocean to which she belonged slowly and regularly breathed. Just below her was a reef, submerged at high tide, and when the sea was rough the waves bursting on it sent clouds of spray flying over her.

At other times when all the world was gentle she could see down through the clear water the waving orange fronds of oar-weed seething to and fro. Or she would lift her head and look out to sea where some grey seals were playing, bobbing up and down, then disappearing, leaving only little swirls of water to mark the places where they had been. Later as they crawled ashore up-wind of her the Wanderer sniffed the smell that did more even than the sight of them to dissipate her solitariness—an acrid animal smell, smacking of the sea.

Two nights and a day followed of ungovernable storm. The seas smashed down on the island, forcing a booming sound out of the living rock. The wind drummed without mercy on every pinnacle and face of stone, bringing arrow-volleys of rain, so swift that they seemed tipped with steel. Then, as a yellow, cloud-splashed morning broke over the sea, the wind died away and left the rollers sweeping along in possession of all the world.

Meeting them, the last of the grey seals plunged away into the haze in the south-west, and the Wanderer was alone. Though she had never been of their company, she felt their going and stared that way long after the last dark head had disappeared. She could not follow them—they were going away from where she had to go. She lay on her rock for hours, never trespassing where the others had been, even now that the island was her own.

As she watched the swell and heard the thunder of the seas the homing instinct insistently began again to disturb her. She moved about irritably; she plunged a few yards towards the water's edge. As if inviting her, a wave bigger than the rest sent a stream of water gliding up the rock almost to her nose. She slid in, and the water took her in the old familiar way, splashed a diamond coronet round her head, and strewed in her path the flowers of the foam. The mermaid was back where she belonged.

Immediately she darted into a powerful current running

N

between the island and a rock. It bore her straight at a razor-edge of stone, but a yard from it she whirled about, challenging all the power the water had gained in two thousand miles' reach of unbroken sea.

She darted forward against the stream where a boat with four oarsmen could not have clawed a way. She stretched out all her graceful length and swept back with the water towards the rock. And then for half a moment she stood upright with the foam boiling past, head and shoulders out, her brown eyes looking a gentle *au revoir*.

She was off! She was sliding through the hills and valleys of the sea, racing north-east as if all the seaweed were waving invitations and all the fragile bells that float in ocean's echoing caves were ringing and ringing her home.

26. The Wanderer Returns

Having been for two years almost always vaguely uneasy,
she suddenly felt at peace.

All that time uncertain and doubting, following the movements of strangers as a stray dog will follow any passing pair
of heels, at last she could feel her way. Though she had
never been in these seas before, there might have been a path
across them as plain as the path to the rising sun.

She passed fleets of fishing-ships, but circled wide of them.
Once a rusty tramp-steamer came plodding out of the north
at such an angle as to meet her on its route. She swam
towards it. When it was almost on top of her she dived underneath, looking up at its barnacle-encrusted and slimy keel.
Approaching the southern coast of Norway she dived more
precipitately as a torpedo-bomber at practice screamed down
the sky directly at her.

Her happiness was partly because of the colder seas and
the increasing darkness of the nights, already seventeen hours
long. A drift of snow excited her so much, after months of
softer weather, that she sidled along the top of the sea and
bit at the flakes.

She saw waves rolling up a new coast ahead—flat, muddy, and open—and she turned north beside it. Very soon she came to a place of islands and fjords, great rock walls rearing out of dark blue water. She wandered into one of these fjords, and sped up it until snow-clad mountains loomed and the dark water had a surface milky smudge from glacier-fed streams. Such water was glorious to her. But she could not pause, and dashed out to sea again, turning north.

She raced on her way, now inside and now outside an island fringe along a coast of splendid cliffs. An ice-field here sent glaciers almost to sea level, and sometimes discharged small icebergs into one of the fjords.

She drove on past an island like a horseman, crossing the Arctic Circle. Then came a night and a day of snow, the dark skies obscuring the brief spell of daylight.

In moonlight she came to a colony of common seals, smaller than the grey seals on whose island she had rested, with darker coats and rounder heads. She had seen groups of this tribe at many places on her journeys. Among these now were some youngsters with steel-blue coats that showed very light and silvery, lazing on some rocks out of the water's reach.

As she swam past these rock shelves the youngsters all came rushing out to stare. Even the yearlings flopped into the water. One of them in his hurry tossed up some pebbles behind him with his rear flippers.

The seals surrounded the Wanderer and peered at her. One swam to her, diving just before collision and popping up on her other side.

A year ago she would have responded with every gaiety of water-play. Now she sank out of sight. One of them followed her down, circling to face her, and she looked for a flash into his eyes before turning and gliding away. They were strangers, and she felt no impulse towards them.

She came to a group of granite mountains straddled in

the sea across her way. She glided between them in a terrific tidal current, which at any other time would have lured her to stay and play. But it gurgled and chuckled and dragged at her fur in vain.

This was a place of gales. Every day or two winds rushed screeching from the south-west, splattering rain, or howled from the north-west in blinding swirls of snow. One midday twilight when the Wanderer was swinging east round northern Norway a cloud suddenly discharged a drumfire of hail and sent her down in a startled dive.

For some time the sun had not risen over the horizon. Most of the hours were dark, except for the occasional shimmer of the Northern Lights. Only at midday did the sun, hidden by the curve of ice-skinned waters on the world's rim, send up slanting beams that were palely reflected on the clouds. Then winter's darkness closed down again until the rising of an ice-ball Arctic moon. Cloud and fog rolled constantly about the seas.

The skerry-fence of islands abruptly ended. In that faint, evasive hour of light the Wanderer saw glimpses of a flat coastline, treeless, like the coasts to which her race belonged. She was in tune with this twilit world. She revelled in its cold and clinging mists, its barren shores, its striding waves, and she danced in the sea, leaping from swirl to swirl at each blink of the moon.

There was a paleness in the sky ahead. Suddenly her heart began to beat so quickly that it almost burst. She passed through the sea like a flying shadow, and so she found the ice again. She raced round the first floating lump, noosing it in a circle of foam.

Presently she was climbing on to a floe and rolling on its covering of snow. She lay for hours gently rocked on the black, shining sea. After a desolation of estrangement her whole being was at last able to rest. The stars gleamed on her shining coat, dark against the purity of the snow. She did not stir. It was as if she had actually become part of the floe, something essential and irreplaceable in the swaying expanse of the Arctic night.

After ten thousand miles of wandering, half circling the Polar world, she had found her way back again where she belonged. So the young swallows find their way unguided from one hemisphere to the other almost as soon as they leave their nests for the first flight, and so the fish sweep in shoals along migration ways through pathless seas.

This pack-ice was not even in the same place as it had been three years ago when she was born. An increase in the air and sea temperatures in recent years has driven the ice-edge back in a line from the White Sea to Greenland, and brought with it a new world of fish. Man flounders bewildered among these changes, but the seals make no mistake. They swim every springtime to the place where the ice-edge is that year; move as it may, they are never early and never late.

While the Wanderer rested on the floe the light airs changed, swinging in from the south-west. As the first puffs blew from this new direction her head lifted and pointed rigidly into the wind. Then she slipped into the sea.

From far away she had heard the din of seals in a cubbing lair, coming as tiny vibrations of the salty air, rather than actual sounds. They spoke to her in the first language her ears had ever heard, and they had the same rhythm as her own heart.

Coming through the floes she passed a mob of harp seals, and did not give them even a passing look. The timidity with which she had approached other seal-colonies was gone.

She slithered up on to a big floe, and found herself surrounded by heavy, anxious-looking pregnant seals, who glanced briefly at her slimness, and then put down their heads and went on uncomplainingly waiting. In these looks at her an emotion was missing that had been present every time she came to strangers since she set out on her involuntary travels. What was missing was the shadow of fear.

They were not afraid of her. She was not afraid of them. They took no more notice of her than if she had been away five minutes instead of three years.

From another floe she could hear the new-born cubs. She swam over eagerly to look at them, and was chased off by the mothers. They did not want a gawking virgin flopping around their offspring.

She skimmed along a tongue of water between two ice-masses, and a seal skipping off one of them plummeted in front of her nose and dived. By the glint of the moon as he went she caught a silver blink from somewhere near the root of his tail, a blink no seal-coat ever gave. She shot down after him to see what it was.

She could dive as fast as he. Her excitement grew as she trailed him, seeing every now and then that extraordinary glitter from the depths of his coat. It was like an extra eye winking back at her. It was like the scaly gleam of a fish. She could not stop following it. When he spun round she dodged and doubled and kept behind him, while he grew almost frantic trying to twist himself to face her.

She had found the painted cub.

The big red cross on his back had long ago disappeared, and she did not know, or he her. But his metal number-tab still marked him out from other seals. And there was something more than that. All through the first and most impressionable year of their lives she had chased this medal-glitter, while he had responded by trying to face her. The behaviour-pattern of the game had been indelibly impressed on both of them. Neither of their natures had been completely fulfilled since they parted in terror so long ago. Each of them missed this undersea performance. In their two-year separation they had changed out of recognition, but each now recognized with delight a design of pursuit that no other seal could trace.

They went twisting through the water, first instinctively repeating puppy movements, then redoubling them with the arrowy speed of youth. Faster, faster yet, up to the surface with a splash, then down to the wonderlands under the floes.

Fast as he went, he could not escape her; when she turned like an eel he turned faster, and his eyes, wild with excitement, incessantly met hers.

Without warning she dived under a shallow ice-pan, came up on the other side among a mob of water-players, and was gone before he could adjust himself to this new turn of the game.

He was not disconcerted in the least. He shot along the surface, somersaulted in ecstasy, sat up in the sea, and barked.

The Wanderer, gliding off alone, heard that bark challenge her short and sharp across the ice, and something stirred in her. When a seal barks in the sea mating play is beginning, and, though she did not know why, this sound made her whole world different.

27. *Mermaid's Wedding*

THAT first mating call to her alone was more exciting than any sound the Wanderer had ever heard.

She was familiar with all the barks and cries usual on the ice, the messages of alarm or hunger, irritability or warning or content. Often during her immaturity she had heard the barks of distant swimmers challenging their mates, and thought no more of them than of the thousand other voices belonging to the sea.

Now she was unprepared no more. Though many harp seals do not mate till they are older, three years of exceptional travel and the unceasing alertness and initiative of loneliness, had hardened and rounded her body and cut short her novitiate. The puppy game of pursuit and escape had suddenly assumed a new meaning. The black dog-like head of the marked seal had focused suddenly in her recognition, distinct from all the hundreds of other males in the breeding-lair. It was a blunt, broad head, the dark colour sharply defined, and extending, like a hound's ears, against the smooth grey of his neck. There was a black saddlemark on his back and sides, matching the one now faintly showing in her own smooth fur. His eyes were large and bold.

As she glided alone through the cold and fragrant water of the lead, so different from the seas in which she had been wandering, a splendid male seal surfaced so close in front of her as to force her to stop suddenly to avoid collision. He curved like a mackerel and faced her, and he too sat up almost perpendicularly in the water and barked.

Harp seals take one mate, and this big leader was asking for her not only with his voice, but with every line of his appealing pose. Before she could back away or sink he ducked under and then sat up again. As she tried to slip aside he leapt to intercept her, ducking as he did so, then sat up a third time barring her escape. It was a sort of dance. Each time he shot so high that half his body was out of water.

Twice her age and powerfully built, he was a magnificent swimmer, and he had played like this before. Each time she tried to get away he forestalled her, so that sometimes it seemed as if he was in two places at once. Always playful, she became uncontrollably excited.

She had never been mastered before, and the sensation was thrilling. He not merely headed her off, he had time to embroider his movements with somersaults or by swimming round her in a ring, turning on his back or side, diving and instantly emerging, blowing and barking.

She dashed at him in a frenzy at being unable to escape and bit him in the neck so that the blood welled out. He made no attempt to defend himself or retaliate; he did not seem to mind, but twisted right across before her to prevent her dashing away. In a sort of ravished entrancement she barked shrilly, half-way between subjugation and terror.

Springing like dragon-flies about the surface, they came to the edge of a floe. She rushed up on to it, and he instantly followed. And out of the water like a rocket behind him came the marked seal. He was almost a foot shorter than his rival, slimmer, younger, but tempestuously enraged.

Before his hindquarters were on the ice he had his teeth in a flashing shoulder, and the big leader rolled against him

just too late to fling him back into the sea by sheer weight. They hung for a second, then began striking at each other with strong-nailed flippers, and a slash of red showed on the youngster's head from the other's teeth.

With ridiculous suddenness the fight stopped. The Wanderer was gone. The combatants stared at each other, and the marked seal lunged fiercely forward. But his rival was too mature and experienced to waste himself fighting with nothing but victory for reward. He side-slipped into the sea with almost cynical ease, and sped away searching for that sleek and supple little virgin, while the winner sat up on the ice and barked and barked, king of an empty castle and looking exceedingly foolish.

The Wanderer, frightened and elated, sped round an ice-headland and raced for the cubbing lair. She dragged herself out of the water there and rested, well away from the others so as to give no offence. She had seen enough fighting for one day.

Several times she crept restlessly about and looked back the way she had come, or stared out at seals playing near by. She did not see either the big leader or the marked seal. Sometimes she wanted to go back to find them. Sometimes she drowsed, and saw again that splendid body half out of the water, the ducking bow, the sheer perfection of strength and speed beyond anything she had ever known, ringing her round and shutting her in and mastering her. Then she would see the playful eyes of the marked seal chasing her, or his savage attack smashing the bigger and heavier leader bodily back over the ice.

Towards evening she got into the water and began nervously swimming towards the lead where all this had happened because of her. Within a minute she grew terrified and spun round, going underneath, heading out away from the ice. After an hour of violent exercise she returned to the edge of the cubbing lair and hauled herself up to rest. Tired, she slept, never even raising her head.

Seal-births occur chiefly at night, perhaps through some evolutionary process of racial defence so that they shall not lie helpless in the full light of day. This was a night of moon, and when the Wanderer woke just before dawn she saw dotted about her a few small, woolly young ones, numbers of older cubs in various stages of baby moult, and some mothers resting or suckling.

Then a pregnant seal near by uttered a heavy groan, quite different from the normal tone of complaint. She lay very still, then groaned again and twisted painfully. Suddenly she lifted herself from the ice, sprawled with her hind-flippers, and a white cub was born, enclosed in a thin, transparent membrane.

Immediately the mother bent herself over it in an attitude of protection. She gently tore the membrane away, and the new-born thing, lean and damp, with a yellowish-white ragged coat, made its first tiny mewing sound. At that the mother put down her head again and contentedly licked its wet coat almost from head to tail in a single strong maternal stroke.

The feeble thing stirred. The mother lifted her head, then bent down in a passion of licking and smoothing the ragged baby fur. Warming it, too, for the new-born cub was practically without blubber under its skin, and but for her body-heat would have shivered to death in the Arctic cold.

The Wanderer slipped off the floe, and began to glide through the sea. She went on, far out of hearing of the great seal-colony, and as she swam the sky grew petal-pink.

She came back after a while, heading towards the point where she had first re-met the marked seal. He was there, as her instinct told her he would be. She dived, raced along, and came up behind him, catching for an instant as he turned the glimmer of that extra eye in his fur.

The game began—the game of puppyhood—but now with every glance and gesture ablaze from the secret fire of life itself. They went so fast that it was impossible to tell which

pursued which. Curved is the line of beauty, and in the
crystal water they drew all the curves of love. They seemed
to gain strength from their own swiftness.

Glancing back at him, the Wanderer darted on to a floe
and lay at its edge, panting and looking down. He shot past
below, flickered on to his back, and glided by again, uttering
long blowing cries. He vanished in a dive, shot up almost
completely clear of the water, fell with a splash that sprinkled
drops over her, and made several swift somersaults.

She stretched out her neck at the edge of the ice, watching
him. He made a ring on the surface of the lead so quickly
that he left an unbroken circle of foam. She leaned forward
till it seemed she must slip off the edge, then drew back. He
spun another circle, and again she crawled forward. But as
he flashed to meet her she withdrew.

At a wilder pace he started to show all his beauty over
again, each muscle's movement by its perfection claiming
the right to fashion other swimmers swift and supple as he.
Untaught, but no less expert at love-play, she began to
move provocatively backward and forward along the edge of
the floe in his full sight. She stopped, stretched her glossy
neck, bent her head and shoulders far back, and raised her
tail high up from the ice, so that her whole body was curved,
supported only by a small part of the belly. In this tense
attitude she remained for a long time with her wooer darting
to and fro below her, each feverishly watching the other.

With a flirt of her shoulders she dropped her fore-flippers
to the ice and turned round several times in rapture. The
movement was unhurried, and gave an incredible impression
of muscular beauty. In the water just beneath her he sat
upright and uttered a deep, hoarse bark of uncontrolled
excitement. At that she began to creep backward and forward again, unable to keep still, her neck all the time out-
stretched to watch for his coming.

Suddenly he shot out of the water on to the floe. In flashing play, their senses of touch, smell, sight, hearing, and taste

all were gratified, and in the same unchecked movement he tumbled her and himself out into the beloved sea. With hardly a splash the mermaid and her lover disappeared.

Only now was the best of the Wanderer's story about to begin.